STUDY GUIDE

to accompany

INTRODUCTORY PSYCHOLOGY: THE MODERN VIEW

Ada M. Smith

Richland College

The Dryden Press
Hinsdale, Illinois

ISBN: 0-03-089416-6
Printed in the United States of America
5678 008 987654321

HINTS TO THE STUDENT

This student workbook is not a "busy-work" device to hamper learning. The proper use of this workbook will shorten your study time and increase the amount of knowledge you can transfer from short term memory into long term memory and increase the amount of retrieval of information. It is important to have enough recitation experience to enable you to learn the material well enough to be able to use it in everyday life and not just at examination time.

In order for learning to be as efficient as possible, you should be (1) interested in the subject matter, and motivated to learn it; (2) aware of what is important to learn; (3) exposed to the material several times in diverse ways; and (4) encouraged to actively participate in the learning process. The workbook material has been designed to provide as much positive influence in these directions as possible.

A brief description of each of the sections for each chapter follows with suggestions as to how these different types of materials can be most effectively used.

I. OVERVIEW

This initial section should be read immediately before you read the textbook chapter. This section is designed to serve as a capsule motivation to elicit interest in the chapter material.

II. OBJECTIVES OF STUDY

This section has the purpose of helping you to identify *what* is important to learn and to give you *active participation* in the learning process by requiring you to list, describe, recognize, draw, identify, define, etc. material relative to the chapter content.

III. PROGRAMMED REVIEW

In this section there are multiple opportunities for the recall of information which you gained while reading the text. This material is designed to further help you to identify pertinent and important concepts for learning plus it gives you an opportunity to check the proper response readily as a check on your recall level.

IV. KEYS TO SELF MASTERY

This section is a summary of the concepts and topics covered in the text. It is designed to be a simple stimulus cue to aid you in putting each topic in context, to make it more meaningful, and to provide some repeated experience with the major concepts discussed in the text.

Once you have progressed to this section the simple stimulus cue presented should enable you to recall various and detailed information selective to the text-book discussion. Should you find that you "draw a blank" on some stimulus word, go back immediately to that section in the text and reread and review adequately. This list gives you a way of checking your memory to see if you are alert.

V. SELF QUIZ

This section contains four-option multiple choice questions which should be used to check your further progress. Answers to each question are provided to the side. Be sure to check your answers immediately after completing the test. Immediate feedback is important.

Since this section represents an over-all test of knowledge of the whole chapter, hopefully, you will earn a near-perfect score. Try to answer the questions without uncovering the correct response column until after you have selected your response.

A last bit of "how to." After you have finished reading the text, have progressed through the work-book sections, and have a few minutes scattered over time between study and examination time turn to the Keys to Self Mastery and review concepts. Should you find that a certain area has escaped your memory turn again to that area in the text and reread it. This is called *overlearning* by learning theorists and is essential for long term retention.

SCIENTIFIC APPROACH TO KNOWLEDGE

Sputnik has started man's race to outer space, yet nothing is quite so exciting as exploring oneself. Each of us has our own list of questions: "Why can't I get along with people?" "What do my dreams mean?" "Why do I sit watching television when I know that I should be studying?" "Why am I afraid to ask a question in class?" "Why are the seats in the 737 airplane like they are?" These questions and many more fall in the purview of psychology.

OBJECTIVES OF STUDY

OBJECTIVE A. Be able to define:

1. psychology ______________________________ p. 3

2. introspection ______________________________ p. 4

3. psychophysics ______________________________ p. 4

4. stimulus-response ______________________________ p. 8

5. classical conditioning ____________	p. 8
6. unconscious motivation ____________	p. 10
7. "symbolized" ____________	p. 11
8. "learned behavior" ____________	p. 11
9. "ability to choose" ____________	p. 12
10. empirical ____________	p. 12, p. 14
11. EEG ____________	p. 12, p. 13
12. research ____________	p. 14
13. public (observable) ____________	p. 14, p. 15

14. repeatable (replicable) ______________ p. 15

15. intelligence tests ______________ p. 16

16. standardized test ______________ p. 16

17. extraneous variables ______________ p. 17

18. hypothesis ______________ p. 18

19. matching ______________ p. 20

20. random sampling ______________ p. 20

21. population ______________ p. 21

OBJECTIVE B. Be able to identify:

1. Wilhelm Wundt ______ p. 3
2. Gustav Fechner ______ p. 3
3. William James ______ p. 4
4. "brass-instrument" psychology ______ p. 5
5. E. L. Thorndike ______ p. 5
6. John B. Watson ______ p. 6
7. B. F. Skinner ______ p. 6
8. Ivan Pavlov ______ p. 8

9. Sigmund Freud ______ p. 9

10. Abraham Maslow ______ p. 12

11. Carl Rogers ______ p. 12

12. Two major categories of psychologists ______ p. 22

OBJECTIVE C. Be able to compare and contrast:

1. structuralism - functionalism ______ p. 4, p. 5

2. behaviorism - psychoanalysis ______ p. 6, p. 10, p. 11

3. humanistic - psychoanalytic ______ p. 11

4. experimental - control group ____________ p. 18

5. independent - dependent variables ____________ p. 19

6. random sampling - biased sampling ____________ p. 21

OBJECTIVE D. Be able to list four of the concerns of psychologists.

1. ____________ p. 13ff
2. ____________
3. ____________
4. ____________

OBJECTIVE E. Be able to restate the three basic criteria of a research project.

1. ____________ p. 14, p. 15
2. ____________

3. ______________________________

____

OBJECTIVE F. Be able to discuss and give examples of the three methods for studying behavior.

1. Naturalistic observation: ______________________________ p. 15, p. 21

____

____

____

2. Testing and surveying: ______________________________

____

____

____

3. Experimental: ______________________________

____

____

____

OBJECTIVE G. Be able to graphically label the parts of an experimental design. p. 19

OBJECTIVE H. Be able to list the major categories and discuss the functions of applied psychologists.

p. 24ff

1. ______________________________

____

____

2. ______________________________

____

____

3. ______________________________

____

____

4. ______________________________

____

____

5. ______________________________

____

____

6. ______________________________

____

____

7. ______________________________

____

____

OBJECTIVE I. Be able to identify and recall pertinent information related to items listed under "Keys to Self Mastery."

PROGRAMMED REVIEW OF MATERIAL

1. _______ set up the world's first psychology laboratory in ____________ Germany, in the year _________.	Wilhelm Wundt; Leipzig; 1879 (p. 3)
2. Psychology may be briefly defined as the _______ __ ______________.	study of behavior (p. 3)
3. Psychology was first considered a branch of ______________.	philosophy (p. 3)
4. Wundt was interested in the structure of the mind. This interest led to a school of psychological thought called ______________.	structuralism (p. 4)
5. The method of study used by the structuralists was called ____________________.	introspection (p. 4)
6. Gustav Fechner is noted for his method of the study of human behavior known as ____________________.	psychophysics (p. 4)
7. The first American to become interested in the new science of psychology was ______________________________.	William James (p. 5)
8. The major emphasis of William James was upon the function of the mind. This led to the establishment of the ______________________ school.	functionalist (p. 5)
9. ____________ was a disciple (student, follower) of William James.	E. L. Thorndike (p. 5)
10. ____________________ was the father of American behaviorism.	John B. Watson (p. 6)
11. Behaviorists limit their study to __________ behavior	observable (p. 6)
12. A modern day behaviorist who studies behavior from an S-R (stimulus-response) mode is _____________.	B. F. Skinner (p. 6)

13. ____________, a Russian physiologist, discovered a form of learning called ________________.	Ivan Pavlov (p. 8); classical conditioning (p. 8)
14. The behaviorists' basic principle for explaining behavior is that all behavior is ____________. This conditioning process is often referred to as *operant conditioning.*	learned (p. 8)
15. John B. Watson's study of human behavior was based upon an S-R paradigm (model). The paradigm for the humanist is S-O-R (stimulus-organism-response). For the behaviorist the O (organism) is considered a ____________ box because he does not choose to consider any data which is not observable.	black (p. 9)
16. A physician from Vienna, Austria, was the founder of psychoanalysis, his name is ____________.	Sigmund Freud (p. 9)
17. One of Freud's major contributions to psychology was his concept of ____________ motivation.	unconscious (p. 10)
18. The __________ psychologists reject the idea that man is controlled by his unconscious thoughts and desires (Freud) or by past conditioning (Watson).	humanistic (p. 11)
19. ________ and ________ are well known humanistic psychologists.	Abraham Maslow; Carl Rogers (p. 12)
20. Much of psychology is a search for the __________ or __________ of behavior.	causes; determinants (p. 13)
21. Brain waves can be detected and measured by the ____________.	electroencephalograph (EEG) (p. 13)
22. The three basic criteria for research are: 1.________ 2.________ 3.________	empirical; public; repeatable (p. 14ff)

23. Naturalistic observations are (more/less) scientific because they are usually not conducted as ________ or________ as those experiments in a laboratory.	less impartially; objectively (p. 15ff)
24. ____________________ are considered tests of general ability.	intelligence tests (p. 16)
25. If you were wanting to determine the general opinion of a population on a particular issue you would use __________ and __________.	surveys; polls (p. 16)
26. An____________ is really nothing more than an educated__________.	hypothesis; guess (p. 18)
27. Once random sampling has occurred the sample is divided into the______________ group and the ______________ group.	experimental; control (p. 18)
28. In the text, smoking and cigarette is called the ______________________.	independent variable (p. 19)
29. The ____________ variable is that variable which should show change relative to the treatment variable (independent).	dependent (p. 19)
30. __________ and __________ are two procedures used to control extraneous variables.	matching; random sampling (p. 20)
31. ________ refers to the total number of all possible cases.	population (p. 21)
32. The two major groups of psychologists are: __________ and ______________.	experimental; applied (p. 22)
33. Applied psychologists use the principles of behavior in many areas of everyday life such as: (1)________________________ (2)________________________ (3)________________________	treating abnormal behavior; counseling; school problems;

(4)____________________________ industry;

(5)____________________________ community;

KEYS TO SELF MASTERY

THE BIRTH OF A SCIENCE

1. 1879
2. Wilhelm Wundt
3. Leipzig, Germany
4. psychology
5. structuralism
6. introspection
7. Gustav Fechner
8. psychophysics
9. William James
10. functionalists
11. 1890
12. E. L. Thorndike
13. John B. Watson
14. behaviorism
15. B. F. Skinner
16. stimulus (stimuli)
17. responses
18. Ivan Pavlov
19. conditioning (classical)
20. Sigmund Freud
21. unconscious
22. psychoanalysis
23. *symbolized* fear
24. *learned* fear
25. humanists

RESEARCH IN MODERN PSYCHOLOGY

1. EEG
2. empirical
3. public
4. repeatable (replicable)
5. naturalistic observation
6. standardized test
7. intelligence tests
8. extraneous variables
9. experimental method
10. hypothesis
11. control

12. experimental group
13. control group
14. independent variable
15. dependent variable
16. matching
17. random sampling
18. population
19. biased sampling
20. scientifically valid

WHAT PSYCHOLOGISTS DO

1. experimental psychologists
2. applied psychologists
3. basic research requirements
4. comparative psychologists
5. primates
6. gestation period
7. clinical psychologist
8. psychiatrist *vs.* clinical psychologist
9. counseling psychologist
10. school psychologist
11. industrial psychologist
12. consumer psychologist
13. engineering psychologist
14. community psychologist

SELF QUIZ

1. Match the following men with the school of psychological thought with which each is most often associated:

a. psychophysics	Wundt		e
b. psychoanalysis	Fechner		a
c. behaviorism	James		d
d. functionalism	Watson		c
e. structuralism	Freud		d

2. Ivan Pavlov, a Russian physiologist was best known for:

   a. operant conditioning — c
   b. learning
   c. classical conditioning
   d. a and c

3. One of Freud's primary contributions to the field of psychology was:
   a. introspection
   b. "unconscious"
   c. conditioning
   d. S-R

   b

4. Choose the psychologist(s) who are considered humanistic.
   a. Carl Rogers
   b. E. L. Thorndike
   c. Abraham Maslow
   d. a and c

   d

5. If you were interested in studying the electrical activity of the brain, one important piece of equipment would be:
   a. sphygmomanometer
   b. Xray
   c. electroencephalograph
   d. EMG

   c

6. Choose the term which is least relevant.
   a. public
   b. repeatable
   c. empirical
   d. scientific

   d

7. Jane van Lawick-Goodall observed chimpanzees in Africa. The experimental method which she used was:
   a. polling
   b. naturalistic observation
   c. surveying
   d. experimental

   b

8. A term most associated with testing and surveying methods is:
   a. extraneous variable
   b. independent variable
   c. dependent variable
   d. a and c

   a

9. In an experiment, one seeks to determine the influence of the
   a. independent variable on the dependent variable
   b. independent variable on the behavior of the control group
   c. dependent variable on the behavior of the experimental group.
   d. dependent variable on the independent variable

a

10. The first psychology laboratory was
    a. founded over 200 years ago
    b. founded at Harvard University
    c. devoted to the study of sex
    d. established in 1879 at Leipzig

d

11. A major difference between an experiment and a naturalistic observation is that one
    a. is subjective and the other is not
    b. studies variables and the other does not
    c. manipulates variables in the situation and the other does not
    d. is scientific and the other is not

c

12. Choose the group of psychologists which do *not* belong.
    a. industrial
    b. school
    c. experimental
    d. clinical

c

13. Extreme cold, which sets up the goose pimples (pilo carple reflex) and shivering, is referred to as a (an)
    a. dependent variable
    b. stimulus
    c. response
    d. control condition

b

14. Psychologists who tend to disregard individual differences between subjects in an experiment are known as:

    a. S-O-R psychologists
    b. clinical psychologists
    c. "human engineers"
    d. S-R psychologists

d

15. The variable manipulated (varied) by the experimenter relative to the question his experiment is designed to answer is known as the

    a. dependent variable
    b. response variable
    c. stimulus variable
    d. independent variable

d

SOCIAL PSYCHOLOGY

One way to find out about an individual and about the society in which he lives is to study the conflicts between that individual and society. If you're a black, a Chicano, an American Indian, a woman, a child, an adolescent, or a drug user, you may feel some conflict with society. When conflicts are not resolved effectively in any society, violence is likely to be one of the results. Violence in retrospect: The Watts riots, the assasination of President John F. Kennedy, the slaying of Dr. Martin Luther King and his mother, the Kent State incidence, Wounded Knee and myriads of others close to you. If you agree with the statement "we are the products of our social environments" what kind of environment would you prescribe? What would you do to rid society of violence, prejudice, alienation?

OBJECTIVES OF STUDY

OBJECTIVE A. Be able to define:

1. social psychology ______________________ p. 31

____

____

2. social influence ______________________ p. 32

____

____

3. social interaction ______________________ p. 32; p. 55

____

____

4. attitudes ______ p. 32; p. 62

5. social facilitation ______ p. 34

6. social interference ______ p. 34

7. social consensus ______ p. 36

8. group dynamics ______ p. 44

9. T-group ______ p. 48

10. feedback ______ p. 50

11. insight ______ p. 52

12. atmosphere of trust ______ p. 53ff

______

______

13. costs ______ p. 56

______

______

14. outcomes ______ p. 56

______

______

15. exchange ______ p. 56

______

______

16. social roles ______ p. 59

______

______

17. inter-role conflicts ______ p. 61

______

______

18. intra-role conflicts ______ p. 61

______

______

19. incumbents ______ p. 61

______

______

20. self-fulfilling prophecy ____________________ p. 62

21. dissonance ____________________ p. 67

22. interpersonal attraction ____________________ p. 68

OBJECTIVE B. Be able to identify:

1. social comparison processes ____________________ p. 34; p. 35

2. Solomon Asch ____________________ p. 39

3. Stanley Milgram ____________________ p. 41

4. Elliot Aronson ____________________ p. 47

5. Muzafer Sherif ______ p. 57

6. social roles ______ p. 59ff

7. R. T. LaPiere ______ p. 66

8. insufficient justification ______ p. 68

OBJECTIVE C. Be able to discuss in detail the two major types of groups.

1. organized groups ______ p. 32

2. unorganized groups ______ p. 32

OBJECTIVE D. Be able to compare and contrast all of of the following.

1. social influence - social interaction ________ pp. 32-61

2. social influence - attitudes ________ pp. 32-55; pp. 62ff

3. social interaction - attitudes ________ pp. 55ff

OBJECTIVE E. Be able to recognize concepts of social comparison processes.

1. social consensus ______ p. 36

2. reference groups ______ p. 36

3. norms ______ pp. 37, 38

OBJECTIVE F. Be able to relate the design of the Solomon Asch experiment and give the results. pp. 39-41

OBJECTIVE G. Be able to demonstrate detailed knowledge of the Stanley Milgram experiment and relate it to parallels in real life situations. pp. 41, 42

OBJECTIVE H. Be able to list five situations in which it is socially acceptable for you to display emotional dishonesty.

p. 44

1. ______________________________

____

2. ______________________________

____

3. ______________________________

____

4. ______________________________

____

5. ______________________________

____

OBJECTIVE I. Be able to list, and discuss three ramifications inherent with the practice of emotional dishonesty.

pp. 45, 46

1. ______________________________

____

____

2. ______________________________

____

____

3. ______________________________

____

____

OBJECTIVE J. Be able to graphically display the chain of events occurring in the interaction between two individuals.

p. 46

OBJECTIVE K. Be able to state and analyze a personal interaction of yours, using the Aronson model.

p. 47ff

____

____

____

____

____

____

____

____

OBJECTIVE L. Be able to describe the character or make-up of a T-group.

p. 49

____

____

____

____

____

____

____

____

OBJECTIVE M. Be able to relate the possible dangers of a T-group and how to remedy them.

p. 53ff

____

____

____

____

____

____

____

____

OBJECTIVE N. Be able to list three positive results of participation in a T-group.

p. 55

1. ____

____

2. ____

____

3. ____

____

OBJECTIVE O. Be able to discuss in detail social exchange. Substantiate your discussion with the experiment by Sherif. p. 56ff

OBJECTIVE P. Be able to describe four roles which you play and tell how your behavior differs in each of the roles. p. 59ff

1.

2.

3.

4. ______________________________

____

____

____

____

OBJECTIVE Q. Be able to list and define three components of attitudes. p. 63

1. Affective: ______________________________

____

____

2. Cognitive: ______________________________

____

____

3. Conative: ______________________________

____

____

OBJECTIVE R. Be able to list and discuss the four psychological functions of prejudice. pp. 64-65

1. adjustive - utilitarian
2. ego - defensive
3. knowledge
4. value - expressive

OBJECTIVE S. Be able to recall and discuss the five factors associated with interpersonal attraction. pp. 68-71

1. possession of valued traits
2. proximity
3. similarity
4. complementarity
5. rewardingness

OBJECTIVE T. Be able to recall and discuss the concepts listed in "Keys to Self Mastery."

PROGRAMMED REVIEW OF MATERIAL

1. ________ is the study of how the ________ behaves in the presence of one or more other people.	social psychology (p. 31) individual (p. 31)
2. Social psychologists are concerned with the ________ as they are part of a ________.	individual (p. 31) group (p. 31)
3. ________ or ________ groups probably influence us (most/least).	informal; unorganized (p. 32) most (p. 32)
4. ________ is one of the most rapidly growing areas of psychology.	social psychology (p. 31)
5. The author divides the study of social psychology into 3 major topics: (1) ________ (2) ________ and (3) ________.	social influence; social interaction; attitudes (p. 32)
6. Factors involved in social influence include (1) ________ and (2) ________.	persuasion; presence of others (p. 33)
7. It has been found that people tend to work ________ and ________ when in the presence of others. This is known as ________.	harder, longer (p. 34) social facilitation (p. 34)
8. Too high a level of anxiety (arousal) tends to ________ with learning new behavior. This is termed ________.	interfere (p. 34) social interference (p. 34)
9. The use of other people as standards against which to judge our own opinion, abilities and behavior is inherent in the ________. We often evaluate our opinions through ________.	social comparison processes (p. 34) social consensus (p. 36)
10. ________ are important when other people influence us by serving as ________ groups.	norms (p. 37) reference (p. 36)
11. Groups demand ________ because ________ threatens social consensus.	conformity; deviance (p. 38)

12. __________ ensues when consensus is threatened.	hostility (p. 38)
13. Solomon Asch used __________ in his experimental design to study __________.	"stooges" conformity (pp. 39, 40)
14. __________ and __________ performed experiments which related to the study of conformity.	Asch pp. (39, 40) Milgram (pp. 41, 42)
15. __________ showed in one of his experiments that conformity may in fact have __________ consequences.	Milgram (p. 43) beneficial (p. 43)
16. One of the most negative products of conformity can be labeled __________.	emotional dishonesty (p. 44)
17. Man has been "socialized" to be __________.	emotionally dishonest (p. 44)
18. Elliot Aronson has diagramed for us the events occuring in an __________ between two people.	interaction (pp. 46, 47)
19. Encounter group is a term which is synonymous with __________ or __________.	T-group (p. 48) sensitivity training group (p. 48)
20. A T-group is usually comprised of __________ persons, being led by a __________ group leader.	5 to 20 (p. 48) professional (p. 48)
21. The two basic goals of a T-group is (1) __________ and (2) __________.	more knowledge of self (p. 48) honest communication (p. 48)
22. __________ is a key which facilitates behavior change by the members of an encounter group.	honest feedback (p. 50)
23. A communication which carries with it an evaluation usually makes the recipient __________.	defensive (p. 51)
24. In order for the T-group to function properly there must prevail an atmosphere of __________.	trust (p. 53, 54)
25. Social interaction is considered to be a __________.	process (p. 55)

26. Physical presence is necessary for __________ __________ but may or may not be present in the case of __________ .	social interaction (p. 55) social influence (p. 55)
27. The formula for a continued social exchange is __________ .	rewards minus costs (p. 56)
28. Muzafer __________ experimentally demonstrated the consequences of ________ and ________ .	Sherif (p. 57) cooperation; competition (p. 57)
29. __________ may be defined as a cluster of ________ that specify the permissible and expected behaviors of people occupying a particular position in a social system.	social roles (p. 59) norms (p. 59)
30. Roles *(should/should not)* be confused with the individuals who occupy them.	should not (p. 60)
31. ________ and ________ conflicts may both be quite disturbing and distressful for the person involved.	inter-role; intra-role (p. 61)
32. The most important social psychological concept of the past twenty-five years is probably __________ .	attitudes (p. 62)
33. __________ may be defined as __________ evaluative reactions to a social stimulus.	attitudes (p. 62) learned (p. 62)
34. The three components of attitudes are __________ , __________ and __________ .	affective; cognitive; conative (p. 63)
35. One of the more popular attitudes for study is __________ .	prejudice (p. 64)
36. __________ serves the same __________ psychological functions as do other attitudes.	prejudice; four (p. 64)
37. __________ may be described as a state of psychological conflict.	dissonance (p. 67)
38. Attitudes *(do/do not)* always correctly predict how a person will behave.	do not (p. 67)

39. "Liking" someone is related to these five factors: (1)__________, (2)__________, (3)__________, (4)__________, and (5)__________.

possession of valued traits (p. 68)
proximity (p. 68)
similarity (p. 70)
complementarity (p. 71)
rewardingness (p. 71)

KEYS TO SELF MASTERY

SOCIAL PSYCHOLOGY

1. social psychology
2. organized - unorganized groups

SOCIAL INFLUENCE

1. social influence
2. social facilitation
3. social interference
4. social comparison processes
5. social consensus
6. reference groups
7. norms

CONFORMITY AND OBEDIENCE

1. Asch experiment
2. Milgram experiment
3. group dynamics
4. emotional dishonesty

COMMUNICATION PROBLEMS

1. sensitivity training
2. encounter group
3. T-group
4. feedback
5. insight
6. trust

SOCIAL INTERACTION

SOCIAL EXCHANGE

1. rewarding
2. costs

3. outcomes
4. exchange
5. outgroup
6. ingroup

SOCIAL ROLES

1. inter-role conflicts
2. intra-role conflicts
3. incumbents
4. self-fulfilling prophecy

ATTITUDES

1. affective component
2. cognitive component
3. prejudice and its functions
4. R. T. LaPiere
5. dissonance
6. insufficient justification
7. interpersonal attraction
8. possession of valued traits
9. proximity
10. similarity
11. complementarity
12. rewardingness

SELF QUIZ

1. Social psychologists deal with — d
   a. introspection
   b. "social animals"
   c. individual behavior in groups
   d. b and c

2. What happens in a group is mostly determined by — d
   a. the age and sex of the leader
   b. the reason it was formed
   c. the number of members
   d. who talks to whom and how much

3. An attitude includes all but which of the following factors — d
   a. emotion
   b. a predisposition toward behavior
   c. a cognitive belief
   d. eagerness for change

4. When society expects a physician to be humane, sympathetic, all-knowing, it is asking that he — a
   a. play the appropriate role
   b. become a "big brother"
   c. set an example for others
   d. live up to the proper status

5. Norms can best be described as — b
   a. rules set by the law
   b. standards shared by a majority of the members of society
   c. universal rules of conduct
   d. a and c

6. An individual is *least* likely to conform to group pressure if the — d
   a. individual is a woman
   b. individual has an "authoritarian personality"
   c. other members are in unanimous agreement
   d. group is very small

7. An industrial psychologist would arrange which of the following work settings to get the greatest productivity out of the workers? — c
   a. place each individual alone in a cubicle to perform their duties.
   b. have three to five people in a small room, each person performing different tasks.
   c. have ten people performing the same task in one room.
   d. none of the above.

8. A student studied for an exam alone but was asked to take the exam in the presence of 40-50 others. The student thought he had mastered the material prior to examination but found that he scored 78. Which of the below could possibly account for the lower score? d

   a. social facilitation
   b. social consensus
   c. a and b
   d. social interference

9. The social principle(s) which is (are) *not* operative in the old cliché "birds of a feather flock together" may be identified as d

   a. social consensus
   b. reference groups
   c. social norms
   d. dissonance

10. In a classroom discussion one student voices an opinion which is contrary to 90% of those present. You may expect a reaction of ______ by the 90%. c

    a. understanding
    b. agreement
    c. hostility
    d. confidence

11. Solomon Asch and Stanley Milgram performed experiments related to b

    a. learning
    b. conformity
    c. punishment
    d. attitude formation

12. Identify the positive rewards for conformity to group norms. d

    a. it can liberate us from the commands of an authority.
    b. it can free us from having to make a conscious decision about each action which we take.
    c. emotional dishonesty
    d. a and b

13. Since most of us have been socialized into practicing emotional dishonesty, communication problems arise and we seek help to try and alleviate these problems. Where would we find such help? d

    a. sensitivity training group
    b. T-group
    c. encounter group
    d. all of the above

14. One of the most important factors in the T-group which can help bring about positive behavioral change is a

    a. honest feedback
    b. evaluations
    c. judgments
    d. a and b

15. Which of the following is *not* a function of a T-group leader? d

    a. tries to establish an openness norm
    b. keeps the conversation of the "feeling" level
    c. lends support to members who risk and become "targets" for attack
    d. most importantly, he evaluates and makes judgments about the group members.

16. You met a good looking girl in the hall last week and you want the relationship to be sustained. Which of the following thoughts will be operative in your decision? d

    a. you really feel great while you are with her.
    b. she wears a little too much eye make-up for your taste, but then, so do most other girls these days.
    c. she makes good grades in Biology and you enjoy hearing her explain the concepts of that subject. They seem so simple when she talks about them.
    d. all of the above.

17. You are the father of two children. They always seem to be fussing at each other. A spirit of competitiveness seems to exist. In order to change the home atmosphere to a more positive one, you would attempt to involve the children in activities which were — c

    a. competitive
    b. punishing
    c. cooperative
    d. rewarding for one child but not the other

18. You are a counseling psychologist and a client comes to you because he is unable to hold a job. In the therapy session you would want to investigate his concepts of: — d

    a. inter-role conflicts
    b. social roles
    c. intra-role conflicts
    d. all of the above

19. "Blondes are dumb but beautiful" is an example of ______ attitudinal component. — c

    a. affective
    b. conative
    c. cognitive
    d. none of the above

20. Which is *not* a basic function of attitudes? — c

    a. adjustive - utilitarian
    b. knowledge
    c. prejudice
    d. ego - defensive

21. The theory of dissonance focuses upon the individual's — c

    a. need to persuade others to accept his beliefs
    b. changing his position on issues over a period of time
    c. motivation to solve inner conflicts
    d. tendency to act in ways which contradict his attitudes

22. A factor which is *not* a key to "liking."
    a. insufficient justification
    b. proximity
    c. similarity
    d. b and c

a

THREE

HUMAN DEVELOPMENT

A. S. Neill, founder of *Summerhill,* concurs with Freud's judgment that parents determine children's personalities; he believes that "there is never a problem child . . . only problem parents."

B. F. Skinner in his *Walden Two,* a novel about a society deliberately planned to achieve certain ends, proposed that children not be left to grow according to nature. Instead, their entire growth should be regulated by the principles of "human engineering." The "good man" is produced by reinforcement of the conditioning process. Skinner purports that if conditioning were used properly in child care, the psychologist would be able not only to predict but even to plan what each child would become.

Neill and Skinner represent two opposite viewpoints of child rearing practices. Out of which kind of home did you come? Permissive or structured? How will you rear your children?

Are children really just "little adults"? What makes children of one to one and one half years enjoy playing peek-a-boo? Piaget's developmental theory does much to explain the wonderment exhibited by a small child when an adult makes motions to take "their nose off and put it back." A fun activity for the adult but awesome for the child who believes that the thumb of the adult which is sticking out between his forefinger and the middle finger is *really* his nose. A child of two and a half to three enjoys the repetition of stories and songs . . . why not teach them the multiplication tables then when it is fun to repeat the same thing over and over rather than waiting until he enters the third grade?

OBJECTIVES OF STUDY

OBJECTIVE A. Be able to define:

1. development______________________ p. 79

2. innate______________________ p. 86

3. identical twins______________________ p. 86

4. "minorities"______________________ p. 88

5. maturational______________________ p. 89

6. reflexes______________________ p. 90

7. perception______________________ p. 91

8. theorize______________________ p. 97

9. stimulus variation ______________________ p. 96

10. "constructs" ______________________ p. 101

11. sensorimotor period ______________________ p. 102

12. "representational" ______________________ p. 103

13. overt - covert ______________________ p. 103

14. deferred imitation ______________________ p. 104

15. egocentric ______________________ p. 104

16. psycholinguists ______________________ p. 107

17. innate ____________________ p. 107

18. personality ____________________ p. 108

19. attachment ____________________ p. 109

20. stranger fear ____________________ p. 109ff

21. separation anxiety ____________________ p. 111, 112

22. "surrogate mothers" ____________________ p. 111, 112

23. identification ____________________ p. 113

24. Oedipus complex ____________________ p. 114

25. peer group ______ p. 116

26. socialization ______ p. 116

27. puberty ______ p. 116

28. stage theory ______ p. 117

29. psychosexual pleasure ______ p. 117

30. egocentrism ______ p. 121

31. morals ______ p. 123

32. internalized ______ p. 123

33. moral reasoning ______ p. 123

OBJECTIVE B. Be able to identify:

1. two methods used in developmental psychology.

   a. ______________________________ observation (p. 80)

   b. ______________________________ experiment (p. 80)

2. "nature vs. nurture" ______________________________ p. 82

3. David McNeill ______________________________ p. 85

4. Jerome Bruner ______________________________ p. 85

5. Freda Rebelsky ______________________________ p. 88

6. Five reflexes in newborns p. 90

   a. ______________________________

   b. ______________________________

   c. ______________________________

d. ______________________________

____

e. ______________________________

____

7. Wayne Dennis ______________________________ p. 91

____

____

8. Robert Fantz ______________________________ p. 94

____

____

9. Jerome Kagan ______________________________ p. 95

____

____

10. Donald Hebb ______________________________ p. 96

____

____

11. Austin Reisen ______________________________ p. 97

____

____

12. Eleanor Gibson ______________________________ p. 98

____

____

13. R. D. Walk ______________________________ p. 98

____

____

14. "visual cliff" ______ p. 98

15. Jean Piaget ______ p. 100ff

16. object permanence ______ p. 103

17. abstract thought ______ p. 106

18. formal thinking ______ p. 106

19. primary caretaker ______ p. 109

20. Harry Harlow ______ p. 111

21. Erik Erikson ______ p. 117ff

22. oral stage ____________________ p. 118

23. anal stage ____________________ p. 118

24. phallic stage ____________________ p. 118

25. latency period ____________________ p. 118

26. genital period ____________________ p. 118

27. eight stages of Erikson ____________________ p. 119

28. Kohlberg ____________________ p. 123

OBJECTIVE C. Be able to list the factors involved in explaining individual differences.

1. ____________________ heredity (p. 81)

2. ____________________ environment (p. 81)

OBJECTIVE D. Be able to compare and contrast inborn differences and environmental influences. pp. 82-89

OBJECTIVE E. Be able to list the contributing factors which might account for a difference in I.Q. (intelligence) among identical twins reared in separate homes. p. 87

1. ____________________

2.

3.

4.

5.

6.

7.

OBJECTIVE F. Be able to defend the current trend in public schools toward, "enrichment" of the educational environment. Give examples of specific experiments which would lead to your conclusion.

pp. 96, 97

OBJECTIVE G. Be able to match specific characteristics of physical, language, emotional and social development with the relative normative stage of development. p. 92, 93

OBJECTIVE H. Be able to write a short essay question and its response on the subject of perceptual development. p. 97-100

____

____

____

____

____

____

OBJECTIVE I. Be able to describe the "visual cliff" experiment. p. 98

____

____

____

____

____

OBJECTIVE J. Be able to discuss "intelligence" from a historical perspective. p. 100

____

____

____

____

____

OBJECTIVE K. Be able to list and discuss in depth the four major stages in cognitive development as proposed by Jean Piaget.

pp. 101ff

1. ____

2. ____

3. ____

4. ____

OBJECTIVE L. Be able to recognize and define two aspects of the attachment process.

p. 109

1. ____

2.

OBJECTIVE M. Be able to relate the implications of the Harry Harlow "surrogate mother" experiments. p. 111-113

OBJECTIVE N. Be able to give two examples of behavior related to the Oedipus complex and explain the underlying principles. p. 113-114

OBJECTIVE O. Be able to discuss factors relative to the process of *socialization*. p. 116

OBJECTIVE P. Be able to compare and contrast the theories of Freud and Erik Erikson. p. 117ff

____

____

____

____

____

____

OBJECTIVE Q. Be able to list and describe the five stages of Freud's theory of normal development. Relate each stage to the period in life when they normally appear. p. 118

1. ______________________________

____

____

2. ______________________________

____

____

3. ______________________________

____

____

4. ______________________________

____

____

5. ______________________________

____

____

OBJECTIVE R. Be able to discuss the **crisis** relative to Erikson's eight developmental stages.

p. 119-120

1. ____

2. ____

3. ____

4. ____

5. ____

6. ____

7. ____

8. ____

OBJECTIVE S. Be able to give three examples of how sex typing and sex-role identification occur.

p. 122

1.____________________

2.____________________

3.____________________

OBJECTIVE T. Be able to discuss in detail the development of morality.

p. 123-125

OBJECTIVE U. Be able to identify the six steps in Kohlberg's theory of moral development.

1.____________________

2.____________________

3. ____________________

____

____

4. ____________________

____

____

5. ____________________

____

____

6. ____________________

____

____

OBJECTIVE V. Be able to recall information related to concepts in "Keys to Self Mastery."

PROGRAMMED REVIEW

1. The normal process of ________ implies that man's behavior and being undergo constant ________.	development (p. 79) change (p. 79)
2. One of the aims of developmental psychologists is to describe the ________ of behavior.	predictability (p. 80)
3. The methods used in studies of development are primarily ________ and ________.	observation; experiment (p. 80)
4. When one expects that brothers and sisters will be more alike in height and weight than will they when compared to their neighbors, you are taking into account ________ ( ) differences.	hereditary (inborn) (p. 81)
5. Many individual differences are transmitted through the ________ from parents to children.	genes (p. 81)

6. ____________ is another big factor which helps to explain why we are like we are.	environment (p. 81)
7. Heredity versus environment is also referred to as ________ ________ ________.	nature vs. nurture (p. 82)
8. Many psychologists believe that there are certain ____________ characteristics shared by the species.	universal (p. 85)
9. Jerome Bruner believes that human infants may be born with ________________ for learning certain kinds of rules.	predispositions (p. 85)
10. __________ __________ are the best subjects to use in the study of the nature - nurture controversy.	identical twins (p. 86)
11. Processes (crawling, walking, etc.) which are primarily influenced by the genetic rather than the environmental elements are often referred to as ________________ .	maturational (p. 89)
12. Involuntary and unlearned responses to certain stimulus are called ____________.	reflexes (p. 90)
13. ____________ and ____________ are two of the more common reflexes.	moro; rooting (p. 90)
14. ____________ development occurs in environments where children are not allowed to crawl.	retarded (p. 91)
15. Jerome Kagan used ________ __________ as visual stimuli to study infant reactions.	three-dimensional faces (p. 95)
16. ________________ performed experiments which studied the affects of enriching the environment.	Donald Hebb (p. 96)
17. Studies indicate that ___________ ___________ is largely complete by about eight years of age.	perceptual development (p. 97)
18. Gibson used the ____________ ____________ apparatus to investigate the appearance of depth perception in children.	visual cliff (p. 98)

19. Intelligence is now being thought of as an entity which *(may/may not)* be measured by a rigid test.	may not (p. 100)
20. ____________ is the most prominent theorizer in the field of cognitive development.	Jean Piaget (p. 100)
21. According to Piaget, the child ________ the rules of principles of the organized world.	discovers (p. 101)
22. Piaget, while observing children at __________, identified ________ major stages in cognitive development.	play (p. 101) four (p. 101)
23. An important factor in cognitive development is when thought becomes __________. This first appears in Piaget's ______________ period.	mentally reversible (p. 105) concrete operational (p. 105)
24. The principle of ________ explains the ability of a child to discriminate and choose a short fat glass over a tall skinny glass when there is more quantity in the short glass.	conservation (p. 105)
25. Formal thinking is often called the model for ______________.	scientific method (p. 106)
26. __________ are psychologists who specialize in the study of language.	psycholinguists (p. 107)
27. A definition for innate is __________.	inborn (p. 107)
28. __________ refers to the patterns of attitudes and behaviors which make each of us unique.	personality (p. 108)
29. Two aspects of the attachment process are __________ and __________.	stranger fear separation anxiety (p. 109)
30. Harlow used ______________ to study the components of attachment.	surrogate mothers (p. 111)
31. The collection of feeling which a male child possesses because of a sense of rivalry with his father is known as the ______________.	Oedipus complex (p. 114)

32. In an adolescent's bid for independence, conflicts may arise which result in an____________.	identity crisis (p. 115)
33. The onset of adolescence is commonly associated with__________or____________.	puberty (p. 116) sexual maturity (p. 116)
34. Freud:__________:: Erikson:__________.	psychosexual (p. 117) psychosocial (p. 118)
35. Industry:__________:: initiative:__________.	inferiority; guilt (p. 119)
36. In Freud's theory,____________is the important product of a child's identification with the __________parent.	sex-role identification (p. 122) same-sexed (p. 122)
37. __________are the values or standards by which a person judges his actions.	morals (p. 123)
38. The development of the__________predicates whether we may experience__________or not.	conscience (p. 123) guilt (p. 123)
39. Kohlberg identified six steps of____________.	moral development (p. 124)

KEYS TO SELF MASTERY

HUMAN DEVELOPMENT
INTERACTIVE FACTORS OF DEVELOPMENT

1. "nature vs. nurture"
2. heredity - environment
3. universal characteristics
4. predispositions
5. innate
6. identical twins
7. maturational

BASIC EQUIPMENT OF THE NEWBORN HUMAN

1. reflexes
2. "moro" reflex
3. Jerome Bruner

4. Freda Rebelsky
5. Wayne Dennis

PERCEPTUAL AND INTELLECTUAL ABILITIES

1. Robert Fantz
2. "looking chamber"
3. Jerome Kagan

ENRICHING THE ENVIRONMENT

1. Donald Hebb
2. M. Rosenzweig
3. Austin Reisen

PERCEPTUAL DEVELOPMENT

1. R. D. Walk
2. "visual cliff"
3. "mirror writing"
4. "mirror reading"

COGNITIVE DEVELOPMENT

1. "cognitive" development
2. Jean Piaget

PIAGET'S THEORY OF COGNITIVE DEVELOPMENT

1. stage theories
2. sensori motor period
   (birth to about 18 months)
3. preoperational period
   (about 18 months to 7 years)
4. egocentric
5. symbolic period
6. concrete operational period
   (about 7 years to 11 years)
7. mental reversibility
8. principle of conservation
9. abstract thought (no)
10. formal operational period
    (about 11 years to adult)
11. formal thinking

THE ACQUISITION OF LANGUAGE

1. psycholinguists
2. David McNeill

PERSONALITY DEVELOPMENT

1. personality
2. primary caretaker
3. attachment
4. stranger fear
5. separation anxiety
6. Harry Harlow
7. contact comfort

IDENTIFICATION

1. imitation
2. castration
3. Oedipus complex

ADOLESCENCE

1. identity crisis
2. independent
3. "generation gap"
4. peer group
5. activist
6. socialization
7. puberty
8. emotional intimacy

THE THEORIES OF FREUD AND ERIKSON

1. psychosexual
2. oral stage
3. anal stage
4. phallic stage
5. latency period
6. genital period
7. psychosocial
8. eight stages of Erikson

SOCIAL DEVELOPMENT AND INTERPERSONAL RELATIONS

1. peers
2. egocentrism
3. social control

SEX TYPING AND SEX-ROLE IDENTIFICATION

THE DEVELOPMENT OF MORALITY

1. morals
2. conscience
3. moral reasoning
4. premoral
5. conventional role conformity
6. self-accepted moral principles

SELF QUIZ

1. A child who is habitually in trouble at school is said to be "born with a mean streak." The person who adheres to this explanation for behavior would argue for — a

   a. heredity
   b. nurture
   c. environment
   d. a and c

2. Which of the following would be attributed primarily to nurture — c
   a. blue eyes
   b. 6′ 3″
   c. fear of snakes
   d. brown hair

3. The animal species most closely related to man and often chosen for experimentation is — d

   a. rodents
   b. canines
   c. dolphins
   d. chimpanzees

4. Recent experimentations by scientists at Emory University lead one to believe conclusively that — c

   a. humans are unique in their communication abilities
   b. dolphins may be able to use language as well as man

c. no animal has communication abilities as refined as the human species
d. chimpanzees can be taught to use languages which are not transmitted visually.

5. Jerome Bruner posited that human infants may be born with   which could be considered a reason why humans have a greater capacity for language than other species. b

a. universal characteristics
b. predispositions
c. environmental influences
d. none of the above

6. Involuntary and unlearned responses to a certain stimulus such as when the bottom of a foot is stroked and the toes turn up is known as b

a. gross motor action
b. a reflex
c. rooting
d. "moro" reflex

7. Processes which reflect a genetic potential with little environmental influence occuring over time are often referred to as a

a. maturational
b. innate
c. environmental
d. individual differences

8. the most active and rapid growth in the life-span occurs during the c

a. first year and a half to two years
b. early adolescence
c. prenatal period
d. none of the above

9. Opportunity to practice a gross motor skill will enable the individual to overcome that particular retardation in early childhood according to: c

   a. Jerome Bruner
   b. David McNeill
   c. Wayne Dennis
   d. Robert Fantz

10. An experiment on perception using the "looking chamber" has shown that infants as young as three days old can d

    a. discriminate patterns
    b. attend to black and white contrast
    c. observe movement
    d. all of the above

11. Kagan in his experiment used three-dimensional faces as visual stimuli with infants ranging in age from a few weeks to over one year. He found that children ________ spent less time looking at the faces than did the others. a

    a. 13 months old
    b. 27 months old
    c. a and b
    d. 4 months old

12. Perceptual development is thought to be complete by the age of b

    a. ten
    b. eight
    c. twelve
    d. six

13. "Mirror writing" and "mirror reading" could be considered alarming by parents and if their three-or four-year-old child engages in either of these they should be alert and seek help for that child. e

    a. yes
    b. true
    c. no
    d. false
    e. c and d

14. One of the most prominent developers of theory in the field of cognitive development is:

d

a. Jean Piaget
h. D. O. Hebb
c. a Swiss psychologist
d. a and c

15. The child exhibits behavior which is characteristic of the sensorimotor period of development when

b

a. his behavior is completely overt
b. his thinking is representational
c. deferred imitation first appears
d. his thoughts become mentally reversible

16. According to Piaget, a child of six is unable to understand the logic of time, space, causality and quantity. This describes behavior representative of the

c

a. preoperational stage
b. concrete stage
c. a and d
d. symbolic period

17. A child of 5 years chooses a nickel rather than a dime when given opportunity. He does so because at that point in his development his level of thought makes him unable to apply the principle of

a

a. conservation
b. reversibility
c. abstract thought
d. logic

18. Not all persons reach the   period.

b

a. sensorimotor
b. formal operational
c. preoperational
d. concrete operational

19.   is most characteristic of the scientific method.

a

a. formal thinking
b. abstract thought
c. concrete thought
d. irrational thought

20. David McNeill uses the similarities in the acquisition of different languages as evidence that the use of language is — c

 a. concrete
 b. learned
 c. innate
 d. for communication

21. Separation anxiety appears in American children usually between the ages of — d

 a. birth and 6 months
 b. 5 or 6 years
 c. 2 years and 4 years
 d. 12 and 18 months

22. A girl who "dresses up" like mother is displaying one of the important processes involved in personality development - - - that is — c

 a. suppression
 b. repression
 c. identification
 d. honor

23. A key concept(s) relative to adolescence is (one) — d

 a. independence
 b. identity crisis
 c. facial acne
 d. a and b

24. Studies indicate that activists come from — d

 a. passive homes
 b. authoritarian homes
 c. strong peer pressure
 d. activist homes

25. The theories of Sigmund Freud and Jean Piaget are similar in the fact that they are both — b

 a. based upon psychosexual causal relationships
 b. stage theories
 c. phallic
 d. psychosexual

26. Freud placed greater emphasis upon stages as a personality conflict producing periods of life. a

    a. oral, anal, phallic
    b. latency, oral, anal
    c. oral, anal, genital
    d. anal, phallic, genital

27. Choose the terms which are correctly related. d

    a. oral, anal, adolescence
    b. oral-sensory, locomotor - genital, anal
    c. latency, genital, maturity
    d. young adulthood, adulthood, maturity

SENSATION AND PERCEPTION

How important are the senses to you? Very! you say. Yes, life would be very dull without them. Just think how it would be to eat a juicy t-bone steak without the sense of taste. What about the senses of hearing and sight? If you had your choice, would you rather be deaf or blind? Do you know why you made your particular choice? This chapter will help to answer many questions as well as raise a few in your mind.

At the Astrodome in Houston, Texas you are able to see all kinds of animation produced on the neon boards when a home run occurs, at Six Flags, you can experience fruit rolling uphill, water running from a suspended water faucet and other "weird" things. Can you explain the relationship of these events to the area of perception? Perception is a psychological process through which we become aware of our environment. It is the area in psychology which attempts to explain why we see what we see.

OBJECTIVES OF STUDY

OBJECTIVE A. Be able to define:

1. sensation ______________________________ p. 136

____

____

2. perceptions ______________________________ p. 136

____

____

3. receptors______________________________________ p. 137

4. neuron______________________________________ p. 137

5. transduced______________________________________ p. 137

6. sensory threshold______________________________________ p. 138

7. absolute threshold______________________________________ p. 138

8. differential threshold______________________________________ p. 139

9. sensory adaptation______________________________________ p. 141

10. vision substitution system______________________________________ p. 146

11. sound waves ______ p. 148

12. ear canal ______ p. 148

13. auditory nerve ______ p. 148

14. intensity ______ p. 148

15. loudness ______ p. 148

16. frequency ______ p. 148

17. pitch ______ p. 148

18. timbre ______ p. 148

19. decibel ______ p. 149

20. electromagnetic energy ______ p. 150

21. perception ______ p. 157

22. apparent movement ______ p. 154

23. context ______ p. 160

24. illusions ______ p. 160

25. moon illusion ______ p. 160

26. monocular cues ______ p. 162

27. binocular cues ______ p. 163

28. interposition ______ p. 163

29. size perspective ______ p. 164

30. linear perspective ______ p. 165

31. shading ______ p. 165

32. movement ______ p. 166

33. texture gradient ______ p. 166

34. retinal disparity ______ p. 166

35. polarized light ______ p. 167

36. holography ______ p. 168

37. phi phenomenon ______ p. 168

38. autokinetic effect ______ p. 169

39. size constancy ______ p. 169

40. social perception ______ p. 171

41. expectancy ______ p. 171

42. ESP ______ p. 174

43. telepathy______________________________________ p. 174

44. clairvoyance______________________________________ p. 174

45. precognition______________________________________ p. 174

46. psychokinesis______________________________________ p. 175

47. Kirlian photography______________________________________ p. 178

48. altered state of consciousness______________________________________ p. 178

OBJECTIVE B. Be able to identify:

1. expectancy______________________________________ p. 139

2. motivation______________________________________ p. 139

3. sonar ________________________________ p. 139

____

____

4. J. E. Amoore ________________________________ p. 143

____

____

5. taste buds ________________________________ p. 143

____

____

6. four primary taste qualities p. 144
   a. ________________________________
   b. ________________________________
   c. ________________________________
   d. ________________________________

7. primary qualities of the skin senses p. 145
   a. ________________________________
   b. ________________________________
   c. ________________________________
   d. ________________________________

8. cornea ________________________________ p. 151

____

____

9. pupil ________________________________ p. 151

____

____

10. lens __________ p. 151

11. retina __________ p. 151

12. iris __________ p. 151

13. rods __________ p. 151

14. cones __________ p. 151

15. optic nerve __________ p. 151

16. blind spot __________ p. 151

17. optic chiasma __________ p. 151

18. William James______________________________ p. 153

19. Gestalt______________________________ p. 156

OBJECTIVE C. Be able to describe the elements in the perceptual process. p. 135ff

OBJECTIVE D. Be able to list four kinds of energy which excite sensory neurons. p. 137

1.______________________________
2.______________________________
3.______________________________
4.______________________________

OBJECTIVE E. Be able to discuss in detail the signal detection theory and relate it to sensation. p. 139ff

OBJECTIVE F. Be able to relate the phenomenon of sensory adaptation to five life experiences. p. 141

1.

2.

3.

4.

5.

OBJECTIVE G. Be able to list six kinds of senses with which man is equipped. p. 142ff

1.

2. ______________________________

____

3. ______________________________

____

4. ______________________________

____

5. ______________________________

____

6. ______________________________

____

OBJECTIVE H. Be able to list and recognize the seven "primary odors" as identified by J. E. Amoore and his associates. p. 143

1. ______________________________
2. ______________________________
3. ______________________________
4. ______________________________
5. ______________________________
6. ______________________________
7. ______________________________

OBJECTIVE I. Be able to locate the area of the tongue related to the four primary taste qualities. p. 144

1. sweet: ______________________________

____

____

2. sour:

3. salty:

4. bitter:

OBJECTIVE J. Be able to draw the structure of the ear and identify the different parts.

p. 149

OBJECTIVE K. Be able to identify and discuss major concepts relative to hearing.

p. 148ff

1. __________

2. __________

3. __________

4. __________

5. __________

6. __________

7. __________

8. __________

9. __________

OBJECTIVE L. Be able to draw the eye and label its parts.

pp. 151, 152

OBJECTIVE M. Be able to write a short essay explaining why perception is more than sensation.

p. 153

____

____

____

____

____

____

OBJECTIVE N. Be able to list five changes in stimulus that attract our attention. p. 154

1.
2.
3.
4.
5.

OBJECTIVE O. Be able to give an example to illustrate how our attention is attracted by: p. 154

1. movement
2. contrast
3. repetition

OBJECTIVE P. Be able to recognize and define the six principles of perceptual organization according to the Gestalt psychologists. p. 156-160

1. figure and ground

2. proximity __________

3. similarity __________

4. continuity __________

5. common movement __________

6. closure __________

OBJECTIVE Q. Be able to describe the relationships of context and perception. p. 161-162

OBJECTIVE R. Be able to list and explain six most effective cues which allow us to perceive depth and distance using just one eye. p. 163-166

1. __________

2.__________

3.__________

4.__________

5.__________

6.__________

OBJECTIVE S. Be able to compare and contrast monocular and binocular depth curve. pp. 167-168

OBJECTIVE T. Be able to give the pros and cons of parapsychology. p. 174-178

OBJECTIVE U. Be able to recall material related to "Keys to Self Mastery."

PROGRAMMED REVIEW

1. ____________ is a psychological response to a physical ____________.	sensation; (p. 134) stimulus; (p. 134)
2. Stimulation of the ________ ________ is the first step in the process of sensation.	receptor cells; (p. 135)
3. Sensory receptor cells are part of a complex communication system called the ________ ________.	nervous system; (p. 135)
4. Your nervous system is made up of a mass of tiny cells called ____________.	neurons; (p. 135)
5. Energy from different stimuli such as pressure, changes in temperature, radiant energy or mechanical energy is changed into ________ ________.	electrochemical impulses; (p. 135)
6. The lower limit of sensitivity is called the ________ ________.	absolute threshold; (p. 136)
7. The smallest amount of stimulus *change* that can be detected is called the ________ ________.	differential threshold; (p. 137)
8. The sensory threshold concept as an explanation for *sensing* is countered by an alternate explanation known as ________ ________ ________.	signal detection theory; (p. 137)
9. In the signal detection theory two important factors are ________ *and* ________.	expectancy; motivation (p. 137)
10. Expectancy is influenced by the ________ __ ____ ____________ of the signal.	probability of the occurrence (p. 138)
11. Motivation is influenced by the ________ or ________ of a decision.	payoff; cost (p. 138)
12. When a sense organ stops responding to a continuous, unchanging form of stimulation, this phenomenon is called ________ ________.	sensory adaptation (p. 139)

13. The ______________ of the odorous molecule determines the quality of the odor.	shape (p. 141)
14. The sense of smell depends upon the passage of air through the ______________.	nose (p. 141)
15. Sensory receptors in the nasal cavity which are sensitive to smell are stimulated only by substances which give off molecules in ______________ form.	gaseous (p. 141)
16. The "flavor" of our food is actually a result of its ______________.	odor (p. 141)
17. There are nearly ______________ taste buds in your mouth.	ten thousand (p. 141)
18. Each taste bud contains about __________ taste cells.	fifteen (p. 141)
19. The number of sensitive taste buds ______________ at middle age.	decline (p. 42)
20. The taste cells are sensitive to ________, ________, ________, and ________.	bitter; sweet; sour; salty (p. 142)
21. The __________ contains the largest area of receptors of any sensory system.	skin (p. 142)
22. The skin senses are ________, ________, ________, and ________.	pressure; pain, warmth, cold (p. 143)
23. Pain receptors are found both ________ and ________ of your body.	inside, outside (p. 144)
24. Body position and orientation is possible through feedback from ____________ and ____________.	muscles, joints (p. 144)
25. Gravitational orientation of the body is provided by sensory receptors deep within the ______________.	ear (p. 146)
26. The intensity of sound is measured in ______________.	decibels (p. 147)

27. The decibel level of____________is described as the painful level of sound for most people.	120 (p. 148)
28. Sounds of too great an intensity *(may/may not)* cause damage to inner ear.	may (p. 147)
29. The human eye is not sensitive to____________.	infrared radiation (p. 148)
30. The purpose of eye movements is to____________ the impinging light onto different receptors so that the receptors will not become adapted and stop responding.	focus (p. 149)
31. The colored part of the eye is the____________.	iris (p. 149)
32. The____________of the eye contains light receptors of two types, called____________and____________.	retina; rods; cones (p. 149)
33. The point at which the optic nerve leaves the retina has____________receptors and is therefore referred to as the____________.	no; blind spot (p. 149)
34. The optic nerve from each eye splits in two at the ____________.	optic chiasma (p. 149)
35. Five stimulus changes that attract our attention are: ____________, ____________, ____________, ____________, ____________.	intensity; quality; movement; contrast; repetition (p. 152)
36. The perceptual process encompasses____________ and____________.	selective perception, organization; (p. 153ff)
37. Perceptual organization is determined by____________ and ____________.	learning (past experience); inborn tendencies (p. 154)
38. The reversible figure is an example of____________ ____________.	figure - ground (p. 155)
39. Proximity may refer to____________or____________.	time; distance (p. 156)

40. "Like" elements tend to be perceived together and this is described by Gestalt psychologists as ______________.

similarity (p. 157)

41. __________ is the key concept related to the Gestalt principle of continuity.

sequence

42. Completing a contour which is not complete is representative of the Gestalt principle______________.

closure (p. 157)

43. False interpretations of sensory stimuli are called ______________.

illusions (p. 158)

44. Cues that permit us to perceive the world in three dimension are divided into 3 categories:__________ __________, __________, and __________.

nonvisual cues; monocular cues; binocular cues (p. 161)

45. The converging lines of a railroad track is an example of______________________.

linear perspective (p. 163)

46. Extrasensory perception encompasses the following concepts:______________, ______________, ______________.

telepathy
clairvoyance
precognition
(p. 172)

47. The ability to affect physical events without physical intervention is a psychic phenomenon known as ______________.

psychokinesis (p. 173)

48. A professional psychologist who studies the area of psychic behavior is called a______________.

parapsychologist (p. 173)

49. ______________________is the latest development for taking a picture of energy force fields emanating from the skin.

Kirlian photography (p. 176)

50. An altered state of consciousness may be induced by______________and ______________.

hypnosis, drugs (p. 176)

KEYS TO SELF MASTERY

1. sensation
2. perceptions

EXPERIENCING SENSATION

1. receptors

PROCESSING STIMULUS INFORMATION

1. nervous system
2. nervous
3. energy
4. transduced
5. electrochemical impulses

SENSORY THRESHOLDS

1. absolute threshold
2. differential threshold

SIGNAL DETECTION THEORY

1. expectancy
2. motivation
3. sonar
4. probability of occurrence
5. payoff (cost)

THE IMPORTANCE OF STIMULUS CHANGE

sensory adaptation

SENSORY SYSTEMS

SMELL

1. gaseous molecules
2. J. E. Amoore
3. "primary odors"

TASTE

1. "flavor"
2. taste buds
3. taste cells
4. four primary taste qualities

SKIN SENSES

1. pressure
2. pain
3. warmth
4. cold
5. vision substitution system

BODY POSITION AND ORIENTATION

1. muscles and joints
2. sensory receptors in the inner ear

HEARING

1. sound waves
2. ear drums
3. ear canal
4. intensity
5. loudness
6. frequency
7. pitch
8. timbre
9. decibels

VISION

1. electromagnetic energy
2. infrared radiation
3. cornea
4. pupil
5. lens
6. ciliary muscle
7. retina
8. iris
9. rods
10. cones
11. optic nerve
12. blind spot
13. optic chiasma

PERCEPTION IS MORE THAN SENSATION

PERCEPTION
SELECTIVE RESPONDING

1. intensity
2. quality

3. movement
4. contrast
5. repetition
6. expectancy
7. motivation

PERCEPTION OF OBJECTS

1. perceptual organization
2. apparent movement
3. Gestalt
4. figure and ground
5. proximity
6. similarity
7. continuity
8. common movement
9. closure

THE INFLUENCE OF CONTEXT

1. context
2. illusions
3. moon illusion

PERCEPTION OF DISTANCE AND DEPTH

1. nonvisual depth cues
2. monocular depth and distance cues
3. interposition
4. size perspective
5. linear perspective
6. movement
7. texture gradient
8. binocular depth cues
9. retinal disparity
10. polarized light
11. holography

PERCEPTION OF APPARENT MOVEMENT

1. *phi* phenomenon
2. autokinetic effect

PERCEPTUAL PERCEPTION

size constancy
social perception
expectancy
motivation

EXTRASENSORY PERCEPTION

1. ESP
2. telepathy
3. clairvoyance
4. precognition
5. psychokinesis
6. Kirlian photography
7. altered state of consciousness

SELF QUIZ

1. The neural mechanisms on and in the body which are stimulated by pain, pressure, heat, and cold are referred to as d

   a. axons
   b. conductors
   c. neutral fibers
   d. receptors

2. The neural mechanisms active when an individual is tasting the sweetness of an ice cream cone are: b

   a. motor neurons
   b. sensory neurons
   c. efferent fibers
   d. synapses

3. The point at which a man first can hear the sound of an approaching car is the a

   a. absolute threshold
   b. terminal threshold
   c. decibel
   d. difference threshold

4. Under optional conditions man's sensory capacities b

   a. have more extended ranges than those of any other animals
   b. enable him to distinguish thousands of different colors and smells
   c. are independent of the influences of the other senses
   d. enable him to perceive all ranges of light wavelengths

5. The eye works much like a camera. It automatically focuses and adjusts the amount of incoming light. Which mechanism is not involved in this adjustment process? — d

   a. lens
   b. iris
   c. ciliary muscle
   d. cornea

6. Any man which has a retina containing only rods — b

   a. is insensitive to light
   b. is color blind
   c. has only chromatic vision
   d. none of the above

7. The point when the optic nerve leaves the eye is known as the — a

   a. blind spot
   b. fovea
   c. pupil
   d. cornea

8. One feature of the sense of taste is that it — b

   a. cannot be divided into any basic tastes
   b. is greatly influenced by the senses of smell, touch and temperature
   c. is located exclusively on the tip and side of the tongue
   d. a and b

9. The areas of the body which contain the greater number of pressure-sensitive spots are the — c

   a. head and necks
   b. abdomen and bottoms of the feet
   c. fingers and lips
   d. ears and eyelids

10. Pain is unique in that it can be experienced — d

   a. as excessive pressure
   b. as excessive temperature
   c. as excessive noise
   d. through the receptors of every mode of sensitivity

11. A cold hand submerged in cold water will feel — b

    a. cold
    b. warm
    c. numb
    d. a and c

12. The sensory receptors responsible for the feeling of dizziness after spinning around and around are — a

    a. located in the inner ear
    b. touch receptors
    c. located throughout the body in muscles, tendons, and joints
    d. a and c

13. Which set of external descriptors are most important in advertisements involving sky-writing? — c

    a. color, movement, intensity
    b. movement, size, repetition
    c. size, movement, novelty
    d. color, novelty, intensity

14. The retinal image of an approaching train has a rapidly increasing size. The train, however, does not appear to become larger, a phenomenon which illustrates — d

    a. the principle of continuity
    b. the principle of proximity
    c. shape constancy
    d. size constancy

15. A horse standing in a pasture is perceived as a distinct entity that stands out against its surroundings. This illustrates — a

    a. figure-ground relationships
    b. size constancy
    c. the principle of similarity
    d. the use of binocular cues

16. Consider the following figures: XXXOOO***. Seeing three sets of figures rather than nine separate figures illustrates the principle(s) of — d

    a. proximity
    b. continuity
    c. similarity and continuity
    d. similarity and proximity

17. A person trying to read an old letter found in the attic, which is dirty and has some moth holes in it, will possibly be able to make out most of the words because of — b

    a. the principle of continuity
    b. the principle of closure
    c. shape constancy
    d. retinal disparity

18. Which of the following is an example of the *phi* phenomenon? — d

    a. common movement
    b. moon illusion
    c. impossible figures
    d. a motion picture

19. The main difference between illusions and hallucinations is that illusions — b

    a. are subjective and hallucinations are not
    b. occurs when there is apparent external stimulus
    c. are completely culturally determined
    d. can be alleviated by drug usage only

20. The binocular cues are — b

    a. psychological in origin
    b. physiological in origin
    c. necessary to the perception of distance
    d. based upon special volume and complexity

21. On Christmas eve a child who perceives a sound as sleigh bells or reindeer hooves is operating under — b

    a. lack of object constancy
    b. the influence of context
    c. time difference
    d. illusionary circumstances

22. The credibility of ESP can be assessed only through | d

a. research
b. replication
c. weeding out charlatans
d. all of the above

LEARNING

As a philosopher you might ask *why* people learn. As a student you are interested in *how* people learn. What are your objectives for learning? Do these objectives grow out of your own needs and desires, or are they imposed upon you from an outside source? If you have decided that, in general, people learn in order to know (as opposed to getting a grade or in order to get a good job), you still have the question as to *how*. At this point the controversy begins.

OBJECTIVES FOR STUDY

OBJECTIVE A. Be able to define:

1. learning ________________________________ p. 186

____

____

2. inferred ________________________________ p. 186

____

____

3. stimuli ________________________________ p. 187

____

____

4. response ______________________	p. 187
5. conditioning ______________________	p. 187
6. neutral stimulus ______________________	p. 190
7. conditional response ______________________	p. 190
8. unconditional stimulus ______________________	p. 191
9. conditional stimulus ______________________	p. 191
10. extinction ______________________	p. 191
11. reinforcement ______________________	p. 192

12. spontaneous recovery ______________________ p. 192

13. discriminate ______________________ p. 193

14. operant behavior ______________________ p. 197

15. operant conditioning ______________________ p. 197

16. behavioral psychologists ______________________ p. 197

17. shaping ______________________ p. 198

18. successive approximations ______________________ p. 198

19. autonomic nervous system ______________________ p. 199

20. biofeedback ______________________________ p. 200

21. continuous reinforcement ______________________________ p. 201

22. partial reinforcement ______________________________ p. 201

23. interval schedule ______________________________ p. 202

24. ratio schedule ______________________________ p. 202

25. fixed interval schedule ______________________________ p. 202

26. cramming ______________________________ p. 203

27. variable interval schedule ______________________________ p. 204

28. fixed ratio schedule ________ p. 204

29. variable ratio schedule ________ p. 204

30. superstitious behavior ________ p. 205

31. noncontingent ________ p. 205

32. Premack principle ________ p. 207

33. positive reinforcement ________ p. 208

34. negative reinforcement ________ p. 208

35. escape ________ p. 208

36. avoid ____________________ p. 208

37. bait shyness ____________________ p. 209

38. punishment ____________________ p. 209

OBJECTIVE B. Be able to identify:

1. performance ____________________ p. 186

2. reflex ____________________ p. 188

3. Ivan Pavlov ____________________ p. 189

4. stimulus generalization ____________________ p. 193

5. psychosomatic disorders ____________________ p. 195

6. B. F. Skinner__________ p. 197

7. Skinner box__________ p. 197

8. Neil E. Miller__________ p. 199

9. Two kinds of partial reinforcement schedules p. 202
   a.__________
   b.__________

10. primary reinforcers__________ p. 207

11. secondary reinforcers__________ p. 207

12. aversive conditioning__________ p. 208

13. internal cues__________ p. 209

14. Garcia effect ____________________ p. 209

OBJECTIVE C. Be able to identify two types of conditioning and compare them. p. 187-212

1. classical conditioning:

2. operant conditioning:

OBJECTIVE D. Be able to identify, in Pavlon's dog experiment, the following items and put out the same terms relative to two other examples of classical conditions given in the text. p. 190-191; 195

1. conditional stimulus ____________________

2. unconditional stimulus____________________

3. conditional response____________________

4. unconditional response____________________

5. neutral stimulus____________________

OBJECTIVE E. Be able to compare the different theoretical positions related to these:

Stimulus—response—reinforcement
and
Stimulus—reinforcement—response

p. 198

OBJECTIVE F. Be able to list four main schedules of reinforcement and relate them to the learning curve.

p. 202-205

1. fixed interval (FI)____________________

2. variable interval (VI)____________________

3. fixed ratio (FR)____________________

4. variable ratio (VR)____________________

OBJECTIVE G. Be able to give three examples of superstitious behavior exhibited by man.

p. 205

1.____________________

2.____________________

3. ____________________

____

____

OBJECTIVE H. Be able to list five secondary reinforcers which motivate man. p. 207

1. ____________________
2. ____________________
3. ____________________
4. ____________________
5. ____________________

OBJECTIVE I. Be able to apply aversive conditioning to achieve a desirable response. (e.g. how aversive conditioning can be used to help a heavy smoker cut down on his smoking). p. 208

____

____

____

____

____

____

OBJECTIVE J. Be able to state a positive action which could be executed by putting the principle involved in the Garcia effect. p. 209

____

____

____

____

____

OBJECTIVE K. Be able to contrast punishment and negative reinforcement (aversive stimulus). p. 209-210

____

____

____

____

____

____

OBJECTIVE .L Be able to recognize and discuss concepts in the "Keys to Self Mastery."

PROGRAMMED REVIEW

1. ______________ is any relatively permanent change in behavior as a result of experience.	learning (p. 186)
2. ______________ ___________ may or may not be an ingredient for learning to occur.	conscious effort (p. 186)
3. ______________ is not directly observable therefore we must use observable behavior or the ______________ of an organism for scientific study.	learning (p. 186) performance (p. 186)
4. Events experienced together in _________ and _________ become associated with one another.	space; time (p. 187)
5. The responses which we exhibit which are automatic are ________________ and are called ________________.	inborn; reflexes (p. 188)
6. ________________ behavior is the simplest kind of ________________.	reflexine; behavior (p. 188)
7. One example of a reflex is the ____________ __________.	knee jerk (p. 188)
8. ______________ ______________, the simplest form of human learning, is based on the stimulus-response relationship of our ________________.	classical conditioning; reflexes (p. 190)

9. Ivan Pavlov's experiment using a dog as the experimental subject, studied ____________.	salivation (p. 190)
10. In Pavlov's experiment, the bell was called a ____________.	neutral stimulus (p. 190)
11. When the dog in Pavlov's experiment salivated at the sound of the ____________, salivation was referred to as a ____________.	bell; conditioned response (p. 190)
12. A ____________ is anything which maintains a conditioned response.	reinforcer (p. 192)
13. The sudden reappearance of an extinguished response *without* ____________ is called ____________ recovery.	reinforcement; spontaneous (p. 192)
14. A bear trained to dance to waltz music probably would not dance to rock music. The stimuli are too diverse to allow ____________ to occur.	stimulus generalization (p. 193)
15. Through training a dog can be taught to ____________ between a bell and a buzzer and respond for reinforcement to one over the other.	discriminate (p. 193)
16. Some persons propose that illness such as ____________, ____________ and ____________ are the result of classical conditioning.	asthma; migrane headache; ulcers (p. 195)
17. ____________ behavior is not based upon reflex behavior therefore classical conditioning is inappropriate.	complex (p. 196)
18. Simple learning can be acquired and eliminated with conditioning techniques. ____________ would fall into this category.	classical; habits (p. 196)
19. ____________ is a technique where learning occurs in small increments called ____________.	shaping; successive approximations (p. 198)

20. It is now known that "involuntary" body activities can be ____________________ with what is called ____________.	operantly conditioned (p. 199) bus-feedback (p. 200)
21. In schedules of reinforcement when 100% of the responses are reinforced it is referred to as ________ ________. Anything reinforcement for a response less than 100% is called ____________.	continuous reinforcement; partial reinforcement (p. 201)
22. Continuous reinforcement produces more ________ learning while partial reinforcement produces more __________ to __________.	rapid (p. 201) resistence; extinction (p. 201)
23. The slot machine is an example of __________ reinforcement therefore when an individual wins they continue to play longer even though they are non-reinforced over several losses.	partial (p. 201)
24. On an interval schedule of reinforcement the subject is reinforced with respect to a __________ variable.	time (p. 202)
25. Reinforcement which occurs randomly, unconnected with any particular stimulus it is referred to as ________________.	noncontingent (p. 205)
26. A ____________ reinforcer is an unlearned reinforcer.	primary (p. 207)
27. Money is a good example of a __________ reinforcer.	secondary (p. 207)
28. Aversive stimuli, such as electric shock is identified as ________________________.	negative reinforcers (p. 208)
29. Positive reinforcers are better known as __________.	rewards (p. 208)
30. If a response is followed by an ____________ stimulus, and the response is then diminished or terminated, the stimulus is said to be __________.	aversive; punishment (p. 209)

KEYS TO SELF MASTERY

LEARNING AND PERFORMANCE

1. performance
2. inferred

ASSOCIATION OF STIMULUS AND RESPONSE

1. stimuli
2. response

CLASSICAL CONDITIONING

1. inborn
2. reflex
3. neutral stimulus
4. conditioned response (CR)
5. unconditioned stimulus (UCS)
6. conditional stimulus (CS)
7. unconditioned response (UCR)
8. extinction
9. reinforcement
10. spontaneous recovery
11. stimulus generalization
12. discriminate
13. psychosomatic disorders
14. habit control

OPERANT CONDITIONING

1. operant behavior
2. operant conditioning
3. B. F. Skinner
4. Skinner box
5. behavioral psychologists
6. shaping
7. successive approximations
8. autonomic nervous system
9. biofeedback

PARTIAL REINFORCEMENT

1. continuous reinforcement
2. partial reinforcement
3. interval schedule
4. ratio schedule
5. fixed interval schedule

6. variable interval schedule
7. fixed ratio schedule
8. variable ratio schedule
9. superstitious behavior

TYPES OF REINFORCEMENT

1. primary reinforcers
2. secondary reinforcers
3. Premack principle
4. positive reinforcers
5. negative reinforcers
6. aversive conditioning
7. escape
8. avoid
9. Garcia effect (bait shyness)
10. punishment

OBSERVATIONAL LEARNING

1. invitational (models)
2. observation

SELF QUIZ

1. Shivering in response to being cold, is a natural response and would be considered — a
   a. an unconditioned reflex
   b. an unconditioned stimulus
   c. a conditioned reflex
   d. a conditioned stimulus

2. The typical sequence of events during early trials of classical conditioning is — a
   a. neutral stimulus, UCS, UCR
   b. UCS, neutral stimulus, UCR
   c. UCS, CS, UCR
   d. UCR, CR, CS

3. Repeated presentations of the conditioned stimulus without presenting the UCS subsequently will produce — d
   a. higher-order conditioning
   b. stimulus generalization
   c. marginal learning
   d. extinction

4. After having a plane crash, a pilot forced himself to pilot a plane every day until the fear of planes disappear, at which time he stopped his daily routine. Ten days later he went to the airport and found that his fear had returned. This example illustrates — b
   a. stimulus generalization
   b. spontaneous recovery
   c. avoidance conditioning
   d. aversive conditioning

5. A spread of efforts from the region stimulated to other parts of the organism, is Parlov's explanation of — d
   a. operant conditioning
   b. classical conditioning
   c. differential conditioning
   d. stimulus generalization

6. Which of the following can be accomplished by using classical conditioning procedures? — d
   a. curing a child from enuresis (bed wetting)
   b. determining the sensory capacities of an infant
   c. causing a student to develop an aversion for books
   d. all of the above

7. When a reward such as a food pellet appears as a result of her pressing behavior it is referred to as a (n)________________ stimulus. — b
   a. unconditioned
   b. reinforcing
   c. discriminative
   d. conditioned

8. Piecework: hourly wages::__________reinforcement: ________reinforcement — d
   a. variable interval: fixed interval
   b. fixed interval: ratio: interval
   c. variable ratio: fixed ratio
   d. fixed ratio: fixed interval

9. An employer who pays his employees the first of every month is using which type of schedule of reinforcement? — b

   a. fixed ratio
   b. fixed interval
   c. variable ratio
   d. variable interval

10. Which of the following is the most effective form of reinforcement once a behavior is learned? — b

    a. continuous reinforcement
    b. variable reinforcement
    c. delayed reinforcement
    d. intervale schedule of reinforcement

11. The method of approximation refers to — a

    a. shaping behavior by reinforcing responses which come progressively closer to the desired response
    b. finding the average value around which a fixed or variable ratio should vary in order to have an effective schedule of reinforcement
    c. determining which stimuli are most likely to evoke the conditioned response
    d. trial-and-error

12. After being conditioned to peck a blue spot to obtain food, a pigeon learns that pecking will produce food only when a buzzer is sounding. In this experiment the buzzer is — d

    a. UCS
    b. a neutral stimulus
    c. a reinforcing stimulus
    d. a discriminative stimulus

13. An experimenter who is in a hurry to teach an animal to perform a complex trick might use all but which procedure? — c

    a. continuous reinforcement
    b. secondary reinforcers
    c. fairly long and variable intervals between the response and reinforcement
    d. the method of approximations

14. A student learns to stay away from the pool tables during a certain hour because he knows that a girl he dislikes will be there then. This example illustrates ________________conditioning. a

    a. avoidance
    b. escape
    c. classical
    d. backward

15. Pavlov: Skinner::______________:________________. b

    a. operant: classical
    b. elicited response: emitted response
    c. bar pressing: salivation
    d. instrumental: operant

16. In operant conditioning, if a click occurs each time a pellet of food is dispensed then a

    a. the click becomes a secondary reinforcer
    b. a typical extinction curve is obtained when the click alone is presented
    c. extinction occurs slowly if both the food and click are withheld
    d. differential conditioning occurs

17. Pressing a bar to terminate a shock is an example of__________________conditioning. c

    a. avoidance
    b. classical
    c. escape
    d. operant

18. *Cramming* is the usual result of a

    a. fixed interval reinforcement
    b. fixed ratio reinforcement
    c. variable interval reinforcement
    d. variable ratio reinforcement

19. If on a picnic you eat too many olives and become ill, then you feel ill upon the sight of olives thereafter, the principle of__________may be operative.

    a. overeating
    b. the Garcia effort
    c. bait shyness
    d. b and c

d

20. In the conditioning procedure where a person is given continuous information about changes that are taking place within a technique referred to as__________ is used.

    a. mind-control
    b. self mastery
    c. biofeedback
    d. autonomic nervous system control

c

MEMORY AND FORGETTING

What does it mean to remember or to forget? I have known people who pride themselves for having an "elephant memory." Still others complain that they have short memories and forget easily. This unit should give you some insight as to the mechanics of memory and forgetting.

The keys to memory if learned and applied will put money in your pocket and better grades on your transcript. How to study and attack a problem for efficient learning can become a part of your repertroire of behavior if you work at it and become an active participant.

OBJECTIVES OF STUDY

OBJECTIVE A. Be able to define:

1. memory________________________ p. 217

____

____

2. recall________________________ p. 218

____

____

3. recognition ____________________ p. 218

4. relearning ____________________ p. 218

5. savings ____________________ p. 219

6. "bits" ____________________ p. 221

7. interference ____________________ p. 221

8. retroactive inhibition ____________________ p. 222

9. proactive inhibition ____________________ p. 222

10. motivated forgetting ____________________ p. 224

11. repression __________ p. 224

12. amnesia __________ p. 225

13. flat worm (planaria) __________ p. 226

14. short-term memory __________ p. 227

15. long-term memory __________ p. 227

16. coded __________ p. 227

17. overlearn __________ p. 229

18. meaningfulness __________ p. 230

19. organization ______ p. 231

20. mental imagery ______ p. 231

21. mnemonic device ______ p. 232

22. narrative chain ______ p. 233

23. self recitation ______ p. 234

24. scheduling your time ______ p. 237

25. closswork ______ p. 241

26. taking tests ______ p. 241

OBJECTIVE B. Be able to identify:

1. Hermann Ebbinghaus ____________ p. 219

2. retention curve ____________ p. 220

3. three stages of memory ____________ p. 220
   a. ____________
   b. ____________
   c. ____________

4. Zeigarnik effect ____________ p. 225

5. DNA ____________ p. 225

6. RNA ____________ p. 225

7. J. V. McConnell ____________ p. 226

8. M. J. Peterson ____________ p. 227

9. Harry Lorayne	p. 229; 231
10. J. A. McGeoch	p. 230
11. association value	p. 230
12. Gordon Bower	p. 231
13. Barbara Manlove	p. 232
14. Bower and Clark	p. 233
15. state dependent learning	p. 234
16. Ralph Rybock	p. 234

17. where to study____________________	p. 236
18. practical study techniques____________________	p. 238
OBJECTIVE C. Be able to state the three basic ways to demonstrate the existence of memory and measure how much of the experience is remembered.	p. 218-220
1.____________________	
2.____________________	
3.____________________	
OBJECTIVE D. Be able to relate identical Hermann Ebbinghaus' contribution to the study of memory.	p. 219

OBJECTIVE E. Be able to discuss the interference theory as it relates to memory. p. 221-224

OBJECTIVE F. Be able to give an example of retroactive and proactive inhibition. p. 222

1.

2.

OBJECTIVE G. Be able to diagram the experimental designs used to test retroactive and proactive inhibition.

p. 223

RETROACTIVE

PROACTIVE

OBJECTIVE H. Be able to discuss the relationship of sleep and interference theory. p. 222-224

____

____

____

____

____

OBJECTIVE I. Be able to compare short-term and long-term memory. p. 227-228

____

____

____

____

____

____

OBJECTIVE J. Be able to recognize and apply six principles which increase retention. p. 229-236

1. overlearning ____

____

____

2. meaningfulness ____

____

____

3. organization ____

____

____

4. mental imagery
   a. mnemonic device
   b. narrative chain
5. self recitation
6. state dependent learning

OBJECTIVE K. Be able to relate the principles for good study habits and apply them to yourself.

p. 236-242

1. where to study
2. scheduling your time
3. practical study techniques

4. classwork ______________________________

____

____

____

5. taking tests ______________________________

____

____

____

OBJECTIVE L. Be able to recall pertinent material related to each of the items in "Keys to Self Mastery."

PROGRAMMED REVIEW

1. The retention of things we have learned is called ______________.	memory (p. 217)
2. ______________ is a term used to indicate when retention is poor.	forgetting (p. 218)
3. ______________ exams usually show one's ability to recognize what they have learned.	multiple choice (p. 219)
4. An ______________ exam would be an example of a measurement tool for ______________.	essay; recall (p. 218-219)
5. Retention can be measured in terms of ______________, ______________, or ______________ needed for relearning.	decrease in time; number of errors; number of trials (p. 219)
6. ______________ was the first psychologist to use savings as a method of measuring ______________.	Hermann Ebbinghaus; memory (p. 219)
7. Ebbinghaus used ______________ to study memory.	nonsense syllables (p. 219)

8. Psychologists have identified three stages of memory: ____________, ____________, and ____________.	storage; retention; retrieval (p. 220)
9. ________ stage of memory could be responsible for memory ____________.	any; failure (p. 220)
10. One popular theory of forgetting is that it is due to ____________ with the ____________ process.	interference; retrieval (p. 221)
11. ____________ occurs when earlier learned material interferes with the learning and recall of new material.	proactive inhibition (p. 222)
12. When new learning occurs between learning and recall of old material and forgetting ensues then ____________ is active.	retroactive inhibition (p. 222)
13. The more a person learns about a subject, the less likely it is that ____________ or ____________ inhibition will cause forgetting.	retroactive; proactive (p. 223)
14. Sleep following study apparently ____________ recall.	facilitates (p. 224)
15. ____________ is an example of motivated forgetting.	amnesia (p. 225)
16. ____________, deoxyribonucleic acid, is the substance which serves as a template of genetic characteristics.	DNA (p. 225)
17. RNA is often called the ____________.	memory molecule (p. 226)
18. If you hold in memory any material longer than ________ seconds the material is then in long-term memory.	15 (p. 227)
19. Meaningful organization of items of information is referred to as ____________.	coding (p. 227)

20. The longer you want to remember something, the more ____________ you should do.	overlearning (p. 229)
21. Mental imagery is one of the ways to increase retention or improve your memory. A ________ device will help in this process. The more ________ the device the more effective it is.	mnemonic (p. 232) bizzare (p. 233)
22. ____________ or ____________ of material to be learned increases memory.	rehearsal; self-recitation (p. 234)
23. State ________ learning is related to ________ ____________.	dependent; stimulus generalization (p. 234)
24. State ________ learning refers to the learner's ____________ state as well as his ____________.	internal physiological; external surroundings (p. 234)
25. Recall is enhanced if the subject is in like state for both ________ and ________ situations.	training; recall (p. 235)
26. The important keys to better study habits include ____________, ____________, ____________, ____________, ____________.	set place to study; time schedule; practical study techniques; classwork; taking tests;
27. ________ study for much more than an ______ without a short break.	never; hour
28. The best time to study is ____________ and ____________ class in order to take advantage of the ________ phenomenon and to help you be ready for class each time.	just before; just after; rehearsal (p. 238)

29. Key words and steps for study relative to practical study techniques are: 1.__________ 2.__________ 3.__________ 4.__________ 5.__________ 6.__________ 7.__________	1. look at picture tables, graphs 2. ask yourself questions 3. read summary 4. ask questions on summary 5. read material 6. recite every paragraph or two 7. review material read (p. 239-240)
30. The __________ the interval between initial study and review, the greater the amount of __________ or __________.	shorter; savings; memory (p. 240)
31. Learning cannot take place through __________, __________, or __________ __________.	osmosis; sleeping with book in hand; playing a tape recorder over and over. (p. 240)
32. Study requires __________.	active participation (p. 240)
33. Without __________ and __________, learning will not take place.	recitation; review (p. 240)
34. The 3 R's of study are __________, __________, __________.	read; recite; review (p. 241)
35. When taking a test __________ leave a question unanswered unless the professor __________ you for guessing.	never; penalizes (p. 241)

KEYS TO SELF MASTERY

MEMORY

MEASUREMENT OF MEMORY

1. recall

2. cue
3. recognition
4. relearning
5. savings
6. retention curve

THEORIES OF MEMORY

1. storage
2. retention
3. retrieval
4. interference theory
5. retroactive inhibition
6. proactive inhibition
7. meaningful
8. motivated forgetting

PHYSIOLOGICAL BASIS FOR MEMORY

1. DNA
2. RNA

SHORT TERM AND LONG TERM MEMORY

1. short-term memory
2. long-term memory
3. coding

IMPROVING RETENTION

1. overlearning
2. meaningfulness
3. organizations
4. mental imagery
5. mnemomic device
6. narrative chain
7. Barbara Manlove
8. self-recitation
9. state dependent learning

HOW TO STUDY

1. where to study
2. scheduling your time
3. practical study techniques
4. classwork
5. taking tests

SELF QUIZ

1. Meaningful learning is best illustrated when the learner — b

   a. gives only correct responses
   b. understands the relationships between the new material and previously acquired knowledge
   c. discovers the correct answers by himself
   d. successfully completes a verbal task

2. Studies of the learning process have indicated that recitation — c

   a. is effective only if it is oral
   b. decreases motivation
   c. improves learning efficiency even if a relatively large portion of proactive time is spent reciting
   d. is more efficient than mere reading only if less than 50 per cent of the learning period is used in recitation

3. A certain professor calls the roll for his class three times a week for four and one half months, but he never learns the names of his students. This failure to learn is probably the result of — b

   a. the ineffectiveness of note learning
   b. the absence of the intention to learn
   c. active participation
   d. b and c

4. The text indicates the best way to study. If we put it into a mnemonic device—SQ3R this would interpret to refer to which of the following sequence? — a

   a. survey, question, read, recite, review
   b. study, question, read, remember, repeat
   c. study, question, review, respond, recall
   d. survey, question, read, remember, results

5. Which of the following is a reason that recitation is an aid to improving academic performance? — d
   a. periods of recitation serve as rests in between periods of steady reading
   b. recitation blocks out other kinds of stimuli which may be distracting
   c. recitation is intentional, while most other study techniques are incidental
   d. recitation is the behavior which usually is required in class or on an exam

6. In programmed instruction, having the learner write key words in the blanks involves the principle of — d
   a. positive transfer
   b. distributed practice
   c. intrinsic rewards
   d. active participation

7. Long term memory involves traces which — c
   a. do not represent a change in the nervous system
   b. are permanent but seldom retrievable
   c. have been established by repeated practice on an intense single experience
   d. represent some modification of neural structures which is easily reversed

8. The psychologist who conducted early experiments on the rate of forgetting was — b
   a. William James
   b. Hermann Ebbinghaus
   c. Belo Zeigarnik
   d. Sigmund Freud

9. The general shape of the forgetting curve for nonsense syllables shows that forgetting — a
   a. is rapid at first and then slow
   b. occurs at a constant rate
   c. is immediate and almost complete
   d. occurs at an unpredictable rate

10. A general term which includes the other three is — c
    a. recognition
    b. relearning
    c. remembering
    d. recall

11. Two groups, a and b, learn a list of nine words. Later group a learns a list of eighteen new words, and group b learns an eighteen-word list including all nine words in the previous list. Group a performs better than group b on the second task because — b
    a. sharpening occurs in recall for group a subjects
    b. group b subjects have to reorganize the memory units established earlier
    c. performance in group b is affected by retroactive inhibition
    d. the recall of group a is influenced by redintegration

12. A boy learns to recite the Gettysburg address without making a single error. A year later he tries to relearn the speech and obtains a savings score of 100. This means that the boy — a
    a. was able to recite the speech without errors on the first trial
    b. needed no more trials to relearn the speech than he had needed originally
    c. needed half as many trials to relearn the speech as he had needed originally
    d. required exactly twice as much time to learn the speech originally as he did to relearn it

13. Experiments have demonstrated that retention of previous learning is greater after a period of immobility or sleep than after a period of normal activity. These results suggest that — d
    a. learning can probably occur during sleep
    b. normally active subjects remember less due to proactive interference
    c. normal activity after learning a task results in repression
    d. what happens during the passage of time, rather than the mere passage of time, causes forgetting

14. Which condition has *not* been shown to produce a marked decrease in retention of material learned immediately prior to its onset? c

a. electro convulsive shock
b. prevention of protein synthesis
c. changes in RNA
d. emotional shock

15. Much apparent forgetting is probably the result of a

a. the failure to perceive the "forgotten" situation clearly
b. lack of imagery
c. insufficient practice at memorizing
d. the Zeigarnik effort

16. The Zeigarnik effect illustrates the importance of ______ in memory c

a. perception
b. interference
c. motivation
d. sharpening

17. Ways in which psychologists measure memory includes d

a. recognition
b. relearning
c. reminiscence
d. a and b

18. Various proposed causes of forgetting include d

a. passage of time
b. retroactive inhibition
c. lack of protein synthesis
d. all of the above

19. The memory may be improved by d

a. overlearning
b. incidental learning
c. making associations
d. a and c

20. Retrieval of information is aided if the individual

    a. recodes the information from "bits" to "chunks"
    b. mentally places the material in various locations around a familiar place, such as one's home.
    c. attaches cue words to stored information
    d. all of the above

d

MOTIVATION

Motivation, why people act like they do, poses a basic question for psychology. Why did James Whitman climb the tower at the University of Texas and begin firing on innocent passers by? Why did Cally destroy the Vietnamese civilians by herding them into trenches and firing upon them at close range? Why do some students drink excessively or take dope? Why did you come to college? If you can answer the whys, you may be able to understand the motivation or the reasons for human behavior.

OBJECTIVES FOR STUDY

OBJECTIVE A. Be able to define:

1. motivated behavior____________________ p. 247

2. need____________________ p. 248

3. incentive____________________ p. 248

4. homeostasis ______ p. 249

5. altruism ______ p. 250

6. hunger ______ p. 253

7. thirst ______ p. 255

8. pain ______ p. 255

9. narcotic analgesic ______ p. 256

10. hypnosis ______ p. 256

11. sex drive ______ p. 258

12. estrogen ______________________________ p. 258

13. sensory deprivation ______________________________ p. 261

14. change ______________________________ p. 262

15. exploratory drive ______________________________ p. 263

16. achievement motive ______________________________ p. 263

17. psychological motives ______________________________ p. 263

18. emotions ______________________________ p. 266

19. frustration ______________________________ p. 268

20. anger ____________________ p. 268

21. jealousy ____________________ p. 268

OBJECTIVE B. Be able to identify:

1. primary drives ____________________ p. 248

2. energizers ____________________ p. 249-250

3. David McClelland ____________________ p. 250

4. Abraham Maslow ____________________ p. 250

5. hypothalamus ____________________ p. 253

6. 5 pain relievers ____________________ p. 256

7. Shor and Orne ______ p. 256

8. J. Money ______ p. 259

9. Kinsey report ______ p. 259

10. Masters and Johnson ______ p. 259

11. B. R. Bugelski ______ p. 263

12. adrenalin ______ p. 267

13. aggressiveness ______ p. 268

14. displaced aggression ______ p. 268

15. fear______________________________________ p. 268

16. anxiety___________________________________ p. 268

OBJECTIVE C. Be able to state five instances of behavior that is motivated. p. 247-248

1. ______________________________________

2. ______________________________________

3. ______________________________________

4. ______________________________________

5. ______________________________________

OBJECTIVE D. Be able to match an appropriate incentive with its causive behavior. p. 248

1. rest ______________________________

____

2. cold-beer ______________________________

____

3. sandwich ______________________________

____

4. escape from pain ______________________________

____

5. a grade of A ______________________________

____

OBJECTIVE E. Be able to compare the differences and similarities between *reinforcement* and *incentive.* p. 248

____

____

____

____

____

OBJECTIVE F. Be able to name the six primary drives of man. p. 249

1. ______________________________
2. ______________________________
3. ______________________________
4. ______________________________
5. ______________________________
6. ______________________________

OBJECTIVE G. Be able to state the relationship between primary drives and homeostasis.

p. 249

____

____

____

____

____

____

OBJECTIVE H. Be able to compare and contrast the drive theory and incentive theory of motivation.

p. 249-252

____

____

____

____

____

____

____

____

OBJECTIVE I. Be able to recreate in order the five steps in Abraham Maslow's hierarchy of needs and discuss each.

p. 251-252

1.____

____

____

2.____

____

____

3. __________

4. __________

5. __________

OBJECTIVE J. Be able to tell the relative position of the hypothalamus and the onset of hunger. p. 253

OBJECTIVE K. Be able to explain why Gatorade is a familiar sight at the benchside during athletic contests. p. 255

OBJECTIVE L. Be able to state the sequence which leads to an addiction syndrome. p. 256-257

OBJECTIVE M. Be able to list eight key findings as a result of a survey by Morton Hunt. p. 259

1.

2.

3.

4.

5.

6.

7. ____________________

8. ____________________

OBJECTIVE N. Be able to select five examples of psychological motives and list them. p. 263

1. ____________________
2. ____________________
3. ____________________
4. ____________________
5. ____________________

OBJECTIVE O. Be able to write a list of expectations which you could follow as a parent if you wanted to produce a child who has a high achievement motivation. p. 265-266

OBJECTIVE P. Be able to recall the four basic dimensions of emotional experience and define them. p. 266-267

1. __________

2. __________

3. __________

4. __________

OBJECTIVE Q. Be able to classify the "good" emotions and the "bad" emotions and give seven examples of each. p. 267

"Good" emotions

1. __________
2. __________

3. ____________________

4. ____________________

5. ____________________

6. ____________________

7. ____________________

"Bad" emotions

1. ____________________

2. ____________________

3. ____________________

4. ____________________

5. ____________________

6. ____________________

7. ____________________

OBJECTIVE R. Be able to discuss the role of emotions in everyday life. p. 269-270

____

____

____

____

____

____

OBJECTIVE S. Be able to recall pertinent material related to each of the items in "Keys to Self Mastery."

PROGRAMMED REVIEW

1. The question of ________ he behaves as he does is frequently answered with reference to ________. | why; motivation (p. 248)

2. ________ : ________ :: reinforcement: reward. | goal; incentive (p. 248)

3. ________ is a general term describing a tangible goal object that provides the stimuli leading to goal activity.	incentive (p. 248)
4. ________ is anything that strengthens and maintains any response with which it is associated.	reinforcement (p. 248)
5. ________ ________ are primarily drives that preserve man's physiological equilibrium.	primary drives (p. 249)
6. The process of maintaining body ________ is referred to as ________.	equilibrium; homeostasis (p. 249)
7. Our bodies are designed to maintain a ________ state.	steady (p. 249)
8. ________ energizes and directs you to a variety of food.	hunger (p. 250)
9. ________ ________, a humanistic psychologist, maintains that not all of man's needs are of equal urgency.	Abraham Maslow (p. 250)
10. According to Maslow's theory of need, all anti social needs are not ________ but arise when innate needs are ________ or ________.	innate; blocked; thwarted (p. 252)
11. For the first four levels of need (Maslows theory), man is dependent upon ________ sources.	external (p. 252)
12. Maslow's theory has inherent in it the view that ________ of one level of needs liberates the individual to seek satisfaction of a ________ ________ of needs.	satisfaction; higher level (p. 252)
13. ________ ________ are ________ factors relative to experiencing hunger.	stomach contractions; secondary (p. 253)
14. A feeling of ________ is more likely due to ________ ________ in the blood.	hunger; chemical changes (p. 253)

15. A tiny structure at the base of the brain, the________, appears to be related to the blood stream and hunger.	hypothalamus (p. 253)
16. Some scientists feel that________________________ are learned.	specific hungers (p. 254)
17. The stimulus for thirst is________________of certain cells in the________________________.	thirst; hypothalamus (p. 255)
18. Man can go longer without________________than he can without__________________.	food; water (p. 255)
19. Pain is an__________________________phenomenon while hunger and____________ *is a*______________ one based on deprivation.	episodic; thirst; cyclical (p. 255)
20. The awareness of pain can be reduced by__________ and the technique of__________________________.	hypnosis; operant conditioning (p. 257)
21. Man engages in sex primarily for survival. ________	False (p. 258)
22. The human sex drive is not as dependent upon __________________________ as are lower animals.	hormonal secretions;
23. On the other hand, the sex drive in humans is greatly controlled by external________________such as a certain___________, ___________, that___________.	stimuli; odor; music; special look (p. 258)
24. __________________________studies have given us some insight into________________ behavior.	sensory deprivation; hallucinatory (p. 261)
25. Some psychologists claim that man has an inborn _________________________, while others feel that is_____________through__________________.	exploratory drive; acquired; learning (p. 263)
26. The most prominent example of a learned motive in American society is the______________________.	achievement motive (p. 263)

27. To "keep up with the Joneses" is an example of the ______________________ .	need for pestige (p. 263)
28. Psychological motives include a.______________ b.______________ c.______________ d.______________ e.______________ f.______________	approval; security; status; power; affiliation; hostility (p. 263)
29. The motive to "save money" is more prevalent among __________ families than __________ families.	middle class; lower class (p. 264)
30. Lack of satisfaction for our motives can lead to disturbances in __________ and __________ health.	emotional; physical (p. 264)
31. High need achievement people are generally more __________ to work on __________ difficult tasks than on either very __________ or very __________ tasks.	motivated; moderately; difficult; easy (p. 265)
32. ________ and ________ are examples of "good" ________ and ________ and ________ are examples of __________ emotions.	love; pride; emotions; grief; hatred; "bad" (p. 267)
33. The result of a blocked goal is __________ or __________ .	frustration; anger; (p. 267)
34. __________ is not an emotion but is most often associated with __________ .	aggression; frustration (p. 268)
35. __________ fear and __________ can lead to emotional disorders.	chronic; anxiety; (p. 269)

KEYS TO SELF MASTERY

MOTIVATION

1. motivated behavior
2. need
3. incentive

THEORIES OF MOTIVATION

HOMEOSTATIC DRIVE THEORY

1. primary drives
2. homeostasis

INCENTIVE THEORY

1. hierarchy of needs
2. David McClelland
3. Abraham Maslow

PHYSIOLOGICAL NEEDS AS BEHAVIOR MOTIVATIONS

HUNGER

1. hypothalamus
2. specific hungers

THIRST

PAIN

1. episodic
2. narcotic analgesic
3. controlling pain
4. hypnosis

SEX

1. estrogen
2. external stimuli

STIMULUS CHANGE NEEDS

1. sensory deprivation
2. change
3. exploratory drive

COMPLEX HUMAN MOTIVES

1. achievement motive
2. psychological motives

EMOTIONS

1. intensity of feeling
2. level of tension
3. affective tone
4. complexity
5. adrenalin
6. aggressiveness
7. displaced aggression
8. jealousy
9. fear
10. anxiety
11. role of emotions

SELF QUIZ

1. The motivational sequence consists of — e

   a. need
   b. reward
   c. drive
   d. instinct
   e. a, b, c

2. Homeostasis occurs when — d

   a. a balanced physiological state is maintained
   b. an animal eats or drinks
   c. man shivers vigorously during cold weather
   d. all of the above

3. Which of the following is/are secondary motives — a

   a. an acquired motive
   b. the hunger drive
   c. sexual drive
   d. a motive which serves as physiological homeostatic function

4. Factors which produce hunger include — e

   a. activity in certain areas of the hypothalamus
   b. dryness in the mouth
   c. sleep deprivation
   d. blood sugar level
   e. a and d

5. Which of the following can serve as motives? e

   a. affectional stimulation
   b. desire for competence
   c. physiological states
   d. sensory variation
   e. all of the above

6. Species survival motives include e

   a. need to avoid pain
   b. sex drive
   c. maternal motivation
   d. need for sensory change
   e. b and c

7. Unlike the sexual behavior of humans, the sexual behavior of rats e

   a. is highly cyclical
   b. is instinctual
   c. involves hormonal secretions
   d. is a homeostatic function
   e. a and b

8. The effect of lack of stimulation upon human beings include e

   a. visual hallucinations
   b. auditory hallucinations
   c. increased ability to sustain attention
   d. self-stimulation activities
   e. a, b, d

9. Acquired motives are also disturbed as d

   a. secondary
   b. primary
   c. learned
   d. a and c
   e. innate

10. The motive at the highest level of Maslow's motivational hierarchy includes the desire to — e
    a. be self-actualizing
    b. be respected and admired
    c. have friends and a family
    d. develop one's potential to the fullest
    e. a and d

11. The notion of romantic love is partially the result of — e
    a. the ideal of knightly chivalry
    b. novels, movies, television
    c. perfume
    d. innate mechanisms
    e. a, b, and c

12. A person is likely to be designated as having high achievement motivation if he — e
    a. is unusually gregarious
    b. has become self-actualized
    c. has a desire to attain a certain level of excellence
    d. day dreams of being president of the United States
    e. c and d

13. Factors which may raise a persons level of aspiration include — e
    a. prior successes
    b. frustration
    c. negative reinforcement with successes
    d. informing an individual that he has scored lower than other less competent persons
    e. a and d

14. The hypothalamus plays an important role in emotional reaction because — d
    a. it is an integrating center for almost all emotional expression
    b. it is the location of "pleasure centers"
    c. it controls the autonomic nervous system
    d. all of the above

15. Chronic stress may produce — a

    a. psychosomatic disorders
    b. the "breakoff" phenomenon
    c. love-hate syndrome
    d. a and b

16. Phobias (fears) may occur as a result of — d

    a. classical conditioning
    b. imitation
    c. innate causes
    d. a and b

17. The neurological mechanisms for pain are: — b

    a. in the reticular formation
    b. not clearly identified
    c. understood best by acapuncture experts
    d. disconnected by hypnosis

18. Important sex studies were done by: — d

    a. McConnell
    b. Masters
    c. Johnson
    d. b and c

PERSONALITY

In high school you were required to take all kinds of tests: achievement, interest, vocational, and aptitude . . . maybe even an I.Q. test. As part of your admission requirements to college you were possibly instructed to take the S.A.T. or A.C.T. If you have gone to seek employment, your prospective employer may have tested your intelligence, specific abilities, and sometimes has measured your personality characteristics. Because testing touches most of our lives and because it is an important branch of psychology you will be considering aspects of measurement in this unit.

You have learned that people make judgments of "personality." Is personality how a person looks, acts, feels, or more? After studying this unit you should feel comfortable discussing the four major theories of personality.

OBJECTIVES OF STUDY

OBJECTIVE A. Be able to define:

1. personality ____ p. 279

____

____

2. perception ______	p. 279
3. skills ______	p. 279
4. motives ______	p. 280
5. actions ______	p. 280
6. asseos ______	p. 280
7. id ______	p. 281
8. ego ______	p. 281
9. superego ______	p. 281

10. pleasure principle ______________________ p. 281

11. socilization process ______________________ p. 282

12. reality principle ______________________ p. 282

13. conscience ______________________ p. 282

14. unconscious ______________________ p. 283

15. intrapsychic conflicts ______________________ p. 284

16. constructs ______________________ p. 286

17. introvert ______________________ p. 287

18. extrovert ______________________________ p. 287

19. inferiority complex ______________________________ p. 287

20. birth order ______________________________ p. 287

21. ideal self ______________________________ p. 288

22. approach - avoidance conflict ______________________________ p. 290

23. traits ______________________________ p. 293

24. trait clusters ______________________________ p. 294

25. objective tests ______________________________ p. 295

26. projective tests ______ p. 296

27. psychological interview ______ p. 296

OBJECTIVE B. Be able to identify:

1. Hippocrates theory of personality ______ p. 280

2. Sigmund Freud ______ p. 280

3. psychoanalytic theory ______ p. 280; 281-287

4. Carl Rogers ______ p. 280

5. self theory ______ p. 280

6. learning theory ______ p. 281

7. trait theory ________________________________ p. 281

8. Freudian slip ________________________________ p. 284

9. defense mechanisms ________________________________ p. 284ff

10. repression ________________________________ p. 284

11. projection ________________________________ p. 285

12. reaction formation ________________________________ p. 285

13. Carl Jung ________________________________ p. 286

14. Alfred Adler ________________________________ p. 287

15. phenomenal self ______________________ p. 288

16. humanistic ______________________ p. 289

17. John Dollard ______________________ p. 290

18. Neal Miller ______________________ p. 290

19. Albert Bandura ______________________ p. 291

20. Richard Walters ______________________ p. 291

21. Raymond B. Cattell ______________________ p. 294

22. 16 PF ______________________ p. 294

23. MMPI ____________________ p. 297

24. Rorschach inkblot test ____________________ p. 299

25. TAT ____________________ p. 299

OBJECTIVE C. Be able to compare and contrast the self theory of personality and trait theory. p. 280-281 p. 287-288 p. 293-294

OBJECTIVE D. Be able to compare and contrast the psychoanalytic theory of Freud with the learning theory of personality.

p. 281-287;
p. 289-293

OBJECTIVE E. Be able to recognize and list three basic components which should be a part of an adequate theory of personality.

p. 280

1.

2.

3.

OBJECTIVE F. Be able to name and identify the component concepts which make up the personality structure as described by Freud.

p. 281-283

____

____

____

____

____

____

____

____

OBJECTIVE G. Be able to graphically depict Freud's ideas on the conscious and the unconsious.

p. 283-284

OBJECTIVE H. Be able to list in order the five stages of psychosexual development that Freud described.

p. 284

1. ____
2. ____
3. ____
4. ____
5. ____

OBJECTIVE I. Be able to recall and give an example of the nine defense mechanisms discussed in the text.

p. 284-286

1. ____________________

2. ____________________

3. ____________________

4. ____________________

5. ____________________

6. ____________________

7. ____________________

8. ____________________

9. ____________________

OBJECTIVE J. Be able to state Carl Rogers' conditions for self-growth.

p. 289

1. ____

2. ____

3. ____

OBJECTIVE K. Be able to graphically depict an example of an approach-avoidance conflict.

p. 291

OBJECTIVE L. Be able to identify the three major means of assessing personality and discuss pertinent details as to use and function.

p. 296-300

1. interview ______________________________

____

____

____

2. objective tests
   MMPI ______________________________

____

____

____

____

____

3. projective tests ______________________________

____

____

____

____

____

   Rorschach inkblot ______________________________

____

____

____

____

____

TAT

___

___

___

___

___

OBJECTIVE M. Be able to point out the dangers and problems associated with psychological tests. — p. 301-302

___

___

___

___

___

OBJECTIVE N. Be able to recall pertinent material related to each of the items in "Keys to Self Mastery."

PROGRAMMED REVIEW

1. ______ can be described as the general pattern of one's ______ unique to oneself.	personality; behavior (p. 279)
2. A ______ physician ______ believed that personality type was related to ______ in the body.	Greek; Hippocrates; fluids (p. 280)
3. Sheldon believed that personality was conelated with a person's ______.	body type (p. 280)
4. Freud, a ______, worked on his theory of personality up until his death at age ______.	Jew; eighty-three (p. 281)
5. Freud's practice primarily centered on problems related to ______ and ______.	sex; aggression (p. 281)

6. Contemporary theories emphasize the problems of ________, ________, and ________.	alienation; identity crisis; conflict (p. 281)
7. According to Freud, the personality is made up of three parts: ________, ________, and ________.	id; ego; superego (p. 281)
8. The ________ operates according to the ________ ________.	id; pleasure principle (p. 281)
9. The ________ mediates the demands of the id and the realities of the environment.	ego (p. 282)
10. The ego is part ________ and part ________.	conscious; unconscious (p. 282)
11. The ________ is the basis upon which the ego operates.	reality principle (p. 282)
12. The ________ is similar to what we call the ________.	superego; conscience (p. 282)
13. According to Freud, young children develop a moral code through ________ of ________.	fear; punishment (p. 282)
14. An inadequately developed superego may lead to ________, ________, ________.	impulsivity; inability to abide by customs; little anxiety or guilt (p. 283)
15. One of Freud's basic premises was that people try to maximize their ________ and minimize ________ and ________.	gratification; punishment; guilt (p. 283)
16. Freud linked the human mind to an ________ with only a tip showing which represents the ________ and the bulk being submerged and representing the ________.	iceberg; conscious; unconscious (p. 283-284)
17. Freud attributed all behavior to ________, and mostly by motives of the ________ mind.	motions; unscious (p. 284)

18. Freud felt that ______, ______, and ______ were due to ______ motivation.	slips of the tongue; social blunders; accidents; unsconscious (p. 284)
19. Material in the psyche was likely to remain in the ______, according to Freud, if the material aroused a great deal of ______.	unconscious; conflict (p. 284)
20. The ______ *has several* ______ means of coping with frustration and wording off ______ called ______.	ego; unconscious; anxiety; defense mechanisms (p. 284)
21. When an individual projects his own feelings onto others, he is using the mechanism of ______.	projection (p. 285)
22. A replacement of an unacceptable thought with contrary actions would be ______.	reaction formation (p. 285)
23. Defense mechanisms are used by normal persons to reduce ______ and ______.	anxiety; stress (p. 285)
24. ______ disagreed with Freud's emphasis on ______ and early ______ influence on later personality.	Carl Jung; sex; childhood (p. 286)
25. ______ felt that Freud underestimated the role of man's ______ and his ______ for ______.	Alfred Adler; aggressive instincts; need; power (p. 287)
26. Behavior problems result if one's concept of ______ and ______ are ______ and ______ according to Adler.	superiority; goals; distorted; unrealistic (p. 287)
27. Adler believed that ______ is apt to influence personality.	birth order (p. 287)
28. ______ believes that man can exert control over his own behavior and has the capability.	Carl Rogers; conscious (p. 288)

29. The ______ *the gap between the* ______ self and the ______ self the more unhappy a person is likely to be.	greater; real; ideal; (p. 288)
30. Rogers conceives of personality development is a ______ attempt to reach toward self-growth. This is contrary to Freud's distinct ______ of personality development.	continuous; stages; (p. 288)
31. Rogers feels that the use of ______ cripples and restricts behavior, while Freud assumed that the defenses were necessary for a ______ ______.	defense mechanisms; healthy personality (p. 289)
32. The learning theorist believe that personality is a result of ______.	learned habit patterns (p. 289)
33. Bandura and Walters disagree with Dollard and Millers approach to the study of personality because the latter uses ______ as their experimental base.	lab-animals (p. 291)
34. Responses learned by observation and reinforced by ______ and ______ from other people tend to be repeated. Responses ______ by social rejection are soon extinguished.	praise; reward; punished (p. 292)
35. ______ *leads to very* ______ behavior.	intermittent reinforcement; persistent (p. 292)
36. A basic principle of learning theory is that ______ learned in one situation ______ *to* ______ situations.	responses; generalize similar (p. 293)
37. Bandura and Walters view personality development as a ______ and ______ process.	continuous; individual (p. 293)
38. Attitudes and ______ that an individual tends to show in *most* life situations are known as ______.	qualities; traits (p. 293)

39. Cattell views personality as a ______ of relatively ______.	set; permanent; characteristics (p. 294)
40. Cattell has identified ______ *clusters* and ______ behavioral dimensions.	36; trait 16 (p. 294)
41. The ______ was devised by Cattell to ______ an individual on his ______ values.	16 PF; measure; trait (p. 294)
42. The ______ was first constructed as a practical means for ______ and ______ the behavior of psychiatric patients.	MMPI; diagnosing; predicting (p. 297)
43. The MMPI identifies ______ major ______ of personality.	ten; dimensions (p. 297)
44. ______ tests are usually based on a ______ set of stimuli.	projective; standardized (p. 299)
45. The ______ is a set of ambiguous pictures which art as stimuli to elicit the feelings and conflicts of the person taking the test.	TAT (p. 301)

KEYS TO SELF MASTERY

PERSONALITY

1. perception
2. skills
3. motives
4. actions
5. assess

PERSONALITY THEORY

1. Hippocrates
2. Sheldon
3. Freud
4. Carl Rogers
5. id
6. ego
7. superego
8. pleasure principle
9. socialization process

10. reality principle
11. conscience
12. unconscious
13. Freudian slip
14. intrapsychic conflicts
15. defense mechanisms
16. repression
17. projection
18. reaction formation
19. constructs
20. Carl Jung
21. introvert
22. extrovert
23. Alfred Adler
24. inferiority complex
25. birth order
26. phenomenal self
27. ideal self
28. humanistic
29. John Dollard
30. Neal Miller
31. approach - avoidance conflict
32. intermittent reinforcement
33. traits
34. Raymond B. Cattell
35. trait clusters
36. 16 PF

PERSONALITY ASSESSMENT

1. objective tests
2. projective tests
3. psychological interview
4. MMPI
5. Rorschach Inkblot
6. TAT

SELF QUIZ

1. Hippocrates suggested that — c
   a. there is a criminal type with certain physical features
   b. individuals can be classified according to eight basic interests
   c. personality type is related to "fluids" of the body
   d. there are two personality types, introvert and extrovert

2. In a very general sense, three basic systems of psychoanalytic theory, the id, ego, and superego, represent ________, ________, and ________ forces — b
   a. social, psychological, biological
   b. biological, psychological, social
   c. psychological, biological, social
   d. biological, social, psychological

3. According to psychoanalytic theory. the behavior of an infant striving for immediate gratification of his need for food is activated by the — a
   a. id
   b. ego
   c. superego
   d. reality principle

4. Which of the following is the best example of an emerging superego? — c
   a. a child begins to cry five minutes before feeding time
   b. a child opens every drawer in the kitchen to investigate its contents
   c. a child says "no, no" to himself as he reaches for mothers lipstick
   d. a child consistently refuses to take foods which look like a banana which he dislikes

5. According to Freud, the largest and most significant aspects of mental life are the ______ level of awareness | a

   a. unconscious
   b. preconscious
   c. conscious
   d. superconscious

6. Which of the following would *not* be an important element in the behavioral sequence described by learning theorists? | a

   a. fixation
   b. cue
   c. response
   d. reinforcement

7. According to learning theories, drives for affiliation, approval, and dependency are | d

   a. primary drives
   b. result of fixations at the early stages of life
   c. source traits
   d. learned through associations with others

8. Like psychoanalytic theorists, learning theorists emphasize the importance of | a

   a. early experience
   b. feelings of competence
   c. functional autonomy
   d. traits

9. According to learning theory, which of the following is a probable cause of a person's habit of whining and complaining when he is dissatisfied? | c

   a. depression
   b. unconscious desire to return to childhood
   c. a history of getting his way when he whines and complains
   d. fixation at the oral stage

10. Which method did Cattell use to determine the primary personality traits? c

    a. free association
    b. clinical analysis
    c. factor analysis
    d. projective techniques

11. Projective techniques are thought to be especially useful in revealing c

    a. situational traits
    b. self-actualized behavior
    c. unconscious fears and desires
    d. important childhood memories

12. In the thematic apperception test (TAT) the subject is a

    a. shown ambiguous pictures and asked to make up a story for each one
    b. shown ten cards containing inkblots, asked to state whatever he sees, and then asked questions about his answers
    c. placed in a specially designed situation to test particular personality traits
    d. given a form containing adjectives to which he indicates his reactions

13. The Minnesota Multiphosic Personality Inventory is used to measure the subjects' a

    a. pattern of responses in terms of psychiatric categories
    b. location on the introversian-extraversion scale
    c. degree of frustration tolerance
    d. ingenuity, initiative, and leadership ability

14. The most versatile approach to the assessment of personality is a(n) b

    a. inventory
    b. interview
    c. situational test
    d. projective technique

15. The interview technique which most resembles a personality inventory is the — c
    a. situational test
    b. unstructured interview
    c. structured interview
    d. stress interview

16. A high school senior may have to decide between going to the college which offered him the biggest scholarship and going to the college which he feels is least exciting for him academically. This example illustrates a(n) — a
    a. approach-avoidance conflict
    b. avoidance-avoidance conflict
    c. approach-approach conflict
    d. double approach-avoidance conflict

17. As the distance from a goal decreases, the — b
    a. tendencies to approach and avoid decreases
    b. tendencies to approach and avoid increase
    c. approach tendency decreases and avoidance tendency increases
    d. none of the above

18. Repression, rationalization, reaction formation, and projection are all — a
    a. defense mechanisms
    b. regression behaviors
    c. forms of fantasy
    d. indicators of the presence of neurosis

19. A small child may kiss and hug his new baby brother when actually he greatly resents the fact that he is no longer the center of his parents attention. This example best illustrates — b
    a. projection
    b. reaction formation
    c. regression
    d. repression

20. In contrast to Freud's emphasis on sex as the primary energizing force in the personality, Alfred Adler emphasized the importance of man's — a

    a. will to power
    b. cooperation-competetition conflict
    c. need to overcome feelings of isolation
    d. self-image

21. A humanistic psychologist would be most interested in — d

    a. a reductionist study
    b. the principles of S-R psychology
    c. human engineering
    d. self-actualization

22. According to phenomenologists, the most meaningful understanding of a person's behavior depends on consideration of his — d

    a. capacity for growth
    b. unconscious motivations
    c. social environment
    d. self-concept

23. Evidence shows that aggression is — d

    a. instinctive
    b. the result of frustration
    c. a learned behavior
    d. all of the above

24. Freud's concept of "superego" is similar to what the average person calls — c

    a. "I"
    b. the "it"
    c. the conscience
    d. a superiority complex

25. Defense mechanisms — d

    a. reduce anxiety
    b. distort reality
    c. operate unconsciously
    d. all of the above

26. According to Adler, a child's awareness that adults can do things that it cannot creates d

    a. defense mechanisms
    b. Oedipal conflicts
    c. family conflicts
    d. an inferitority complex

27. According to Kretchmer and Sheldon, personality is determined mainly by b

    a. early childhood experiences
    b. body types
    c. IQ
    d. intrapsychic factors

28. A theory of personality must deal with: d

    a. long-lasting mental states
    b. similarities among people
    c. difference between people
    d. all of the above

29. Which of the following is *not* a projective test? a

    a. MMPI
    b. Rorschach
    c. TAT
    d. word associations

30. Projective tests b

    a. are based on the conditional-response approach
    b. are interpreted differently by each psychologist
    c. are objectively scored
    d. all of the above

ABNORMAL BEHAVIOR

You have learned that defense mechanisms often arise in response to a temporary situation. They are useful to protect the ego from undue anxiety and threat. Paradoxically, even neuroses and psychoses seem to be attempts at health — they are **survival strategies.** Many of these defenses are an attempt to **not feel** pain. When feeling is blocked, the person is less alive and less able to function and to grow. Many people live out their lives with much of their feeling capacity blocked. Others are unwilling to settle for what they see as less than living. They go into therapy.

OBJECTIVES FOR STUDY

OBJECTIVE A. Be able to define:

1. model ______________________________ p. 313

____

____

2. general paresis ______________________________ p. 314

____

____

3. Wassermann blood test ______ p. 315

4. behaviorist ______ p. 316

5. reconditioning ______ p. 317

6. diagnosed ______ p. 318

7. anxiety neurosis ______ p. 321

8. phobias ______ p. 321

9. obsessive - compulsive neurosis ______ p. 322

10. obsessions ______ p. 322

11. compulsions ______ p. 322

12. hysterical neurosis ______ p. 323

13. dissociative reaction ______ p. 324

14. multiple personality ______ p. 325

15. psychosomatic ______ p. 327

16. essential hypertension ______ p. 328

17. psychosis ______ p. 330

18. functional psychoses ______ p. 331

19. organic psychoses______________________________ p. 331

20. delusion of grandeur______________________________ p. 334

21. manic psychosis______________________________ p. 337

22. depressive psychosis______________________________ p. 337

23. manic - depressive psychosis______________________________ p. 337

24. involutional depression______________________________ p. 338

25. remission______________________________ p. 338

26. physiological dependence______________________________ p. 341

27. psychological dependence ______________________ p. 341

____

____

28. impotence ______________________ p. 346

____

____

29. frigidity ______________________ p. 346

____

____

30. masochism ______________________ p. 346

____

____

31. exhibitionism ______________________ p. 346

____

____

32. fetishism ______________________ p. 346

____

____

33. pedophilia ______________________ p. 346

____

____

34. voyeurism ______________________ p. 346

____

____

35. incest ______ p. 346

36. sadism ______ p. 346

37. prostitution ______ p. 346

38. transvestism ______ p. 346

39. transsexualism ______ p. 347

40. homosexuality ______ p. 347

41. mental retardation ______ p. 349

42. mongolism ______ p. 349

OBJECTIVE B. Be able to identify:

1. abnormal behavior ______ p. 307-308

2. Thomas Szasz ______ p. 309

3. maladaptive behavior ______ p. 309

4. psychodynamic model ______ p. 313

5. biomedical model ______ p. 314

6. social learning model ______ p. 316

7. existential model ______ p. 317

8. conversion reaction ______ p. 323

9. hypnosis ______________________ p. 324

10. amnesia ______________________ p. 324

11. fugue state ______________________ p. 324

12. somnambulism ______________________ p. 325

13. depressive neuroses ______________________ p. 326

14. psychosomatic disorders ______________________ p. 327

15. ulcers ______________________ p. 327-328

16. migraine headache ______________________ p. 328

17. hypertension ______________________________	p. 328-329
18. Murray Banks ______________________________	p. 330
19. delusions ______________________________	p. 331
20. hallucinations ______________________________	p. 331
21. schizophrenia ______________________________	p. 331
22. simple schizophrenia ______________________________	p. 332
23. catatonic schizophrenia ______________________________	p. 332-333
24. hebephrenic schizophrenia ______________________________	p. 334

25. paranoia ______________________________ p. 335

26. affective psychosis ______________________________ p. 337

27. delirium tremens (dt's) ______________________________ p. 342

28. heroin addiction ______________________________ p. 343

29. methadone ______________________________ p. 344

30. barbiturates ______________________________ p. 344

31. amphetamides ______________________________ p. 344

32. sexual deviations ______________________________ p. 345

33. primary mental retardation______________________ p. 349

34. Down's syndrome______________________ p. 349

35. cretinism______________________ p. 349

36. microcephaly______________________ p. 350

37. phenylkentonuria (PKU)______________________ p. 350

OBJECTIVE C. Be able to report behaviors frequently experienced which might be considered abnormal p. 308

1.______________________

2.______________________

3.______________________

4.______________________

OBJECTIVE D. Be able to choose terms which are used to describe behavior which is unusual or pathological

p. 309

1.____
2.____
3.____
4.____
5.____
6.____

OBJECTIVE E. Be able to relate the historical perspective of attitudes toward abnormal behavior and its treatment.

p. 311-312

OBJECTIVE F. Be able to compare and contrast the four models of abnormal behavior with each of the other.

p. 313-318

1. psychodynamic model______________________

2. biomedical model ______________________________

3. social learning model ______________________________

4. existential model ______________________________

OBJECTIVE G. Be able to state two consequences of the biomedical model of mental illness.

p. 315

1. ______

2. ______

OBJECTIVE H. Be able to identify and describe the associative behaviors of the five major diagnostic categories of abnormal behavior

p. 318ff

1. neurosis ______

2. psychosomatic disorders ______

3. psychosis ______

4. personality disorders ______

5. mental retardation

OBJECTIVE I. Be able to recite the symptoms of neurotic behavior

p. 319

1.

2.

3.

OBJECTIVE J. Be able to identify and describe relevant concepts dealing with six forms of neurotic behavior

p. 320-327

1. anxiety neuroses: ______________________

2. phobias: ______________________

3. obsessive - compulsive neurosis ______________________

4. hysteria ______________________

5. dissociative reactions ________________________________

6. depressives ________________________________

OBJECTIVE K. Be able to recall four types of dissociative reactions and identify each one

p. 324

1. amnesia: ________________________________

2. fugue state: ________________________________

3. multiple personality: ________________________________

4. somnambulism: ______________________

____

____

____

OBJECTIVE L. Be able to name three of the more common psychosomatic disorders and describe the symptoms. p. 327

1. ______________________

____

____

2. ______________________

____

____

3. ______________________

____

____

OBJECTIVE M. Be able to write five common causes of organic psychosis. p. 331

1. ______________________
2. ______________________
3. ______________________
4. ______________________
5. ______________________

OBJECTIVE N. Be able to state the three major causes of functional psychoses. p. 331

1. ______________________
2. ______________________
3. ______________________

OBJECTIVE O. Be able to describe the behavioral patterns of a schizophrenic and to identify and select the four main sub categories of schizophrenia

p. 331-334

schizophrenic ____________________

____

____

____

____

Four main subcategories

1. ____________________

____

____

____

2. ____________________

____

____

____

3. ____________________

____

____

____

4. ____________________

____

____

____

OBJECTIVE P. Be able to list the four areas of affective psychosis and discuss them.

p. 337-340

1. ____________________

2. ____________________

3. ____________________

4. ____________________

OBJECTIVE Q. Be able to write four categories of persons who have the highest suicide rate.

p. 339

1. ____________________
2. ____________________
3. ____________________
4. ____________________

OBJECTIVE R. Be able to recognize the three major personality disorders and relate pertinent information about each category.

p. 340-349

1. ____________________

____

____

____

2. ____________________

____

____

____

3. ____________________

____

____

____

OBJECTIVE S. Be able to distinguish the three types of sexual "deviation."

p. 345-349

1.

a. ____________________

____

b. ____________________

____

c. ____________________

____

d. ____________________

____

2.

a. ____________________

b. ____________________

c. ____________________

d. ____________________

e. ____________________

f. ____________________

g. ____________________

h. ____________________

i. ____________________

3.

a. ____________________

b. ____________________

c. ____________________

d. ____________________

OBJECTIVE T. Be able to recall the four psychosocial factors which appear to be heart of the causes of homosexuality.

p. 348

1.______________________________________

2.______________________________________

3.______________________________________

4.______________________________________

OBJECTIVE U. Be able to name and give relative characteristics of the first major areas of mental retardation as discussed in the text.

p. 349-351

1.______________________________________

2.______________________________________

3.______________________________________

4.______________________________________

5. ____

____

____

OBJECTIVE V. Be able to recall and recite relevant material about the items listed in "Keys to Self Mastery".

PROGRAMMED REVIEW

1. ____________ is that behavior which poses a problem for the ________ or for ________.

abnormal behavior; individual; society (p. 308)

2. ______, ________, ________, ____________ symptoms, terrifying ________ and ________ experiences are often reported as abnormal behavior.

fears; guilt; unhappiness; physical; visual; auditory (p. 308)

3. A person like Roger or Rosalie is said not to be able to ____________.

cope (p. 309)

4. ____________ claims that there is no mental illness, only rejection of certain types of behavior.

Thomas Szasz; social (p. 309)

5. Freud introduced the ____________ model as a ________ or ____________ between parts of a person's ______________.

psychodynamic; battle; conflict; personality (p. 313)

6. The psychodynamic model stresses the importance of ____________ events on ______________.

environmental; behavior (p. 314)

7. The ______________ model emphasizes variables related to ____________ *such as* ____________ makeup, condition of the ______________, and ______________.

biomedical; bodily functioning; genetic; nervous system; biochemistry (p. 314)

8. A severe mental disturbance caused by ________ is known as ______________.

syphilis; general paresis (p. 314)

9. Syphilis leads to general paresis in about ________ of the cases but the lag time between the initial syphilitic attack and the onset of general paresis is usually ________, ________ or even ________ years.	3%; ten, twenty, thirty (p. 314)
10. The ________ blood test ________ and ________ have just about wiped out the occurrence of general ________.	Wassermann; penicillin; paresis (p. 315)
11. Researchers have found that some violent criminals have an extra ______ ________ in their genetic makeup.	y; chromosome (p. 315-316)
12. ________ reject all psychodynamic notions of ________ conflicts and inferences about ________ aspects of behavior.	behaviorists; unconscious; unobservable (p. 316)
13. Bandura and Walters proposed that much of our personality is acquired through ________, ________, and ________.	observation; imitation; reinforcement (p. 317)
14. ________ believe that what matters is the person's ________, not his ________ experiences or his history of ________.	existentialists; present existence; childhood; reinforcement (p. 317)
15. ________ and ________ are proponents of the existentialist view. They stress the individual's present opportunities and future alternatives.	Rogers; Maslow (p. 317)
16. In the existential model, man is ________ for his ________ behavior.	responsible; own (p. 317)
17. In classifying persons with abnormal behavior it should be noted that all human behavior is ________.	unique (p. 318)
18. The primary ________ of neurosis is ________.	characteristic; anxiety (p. 318)
19. In ________ the use of defenses to avoid or ________ anxiety is ________.	neurosis; escape; exaggerated (p. 319)

20. A ________________ must use a great deal of his ________________ in the effort to control his constant ________________.	neurotic; energy; anxiety (p. 319)
21. A ______________ is a intense ______________ of a specific object or situation that is out of proportion to the actual danger.	phobia; fear (p. 321)
22. Repetitive ____________ or ____________ that rule life are indicative of ______________ behavior.	thoughts; impulses; obsessive-compulsive (p. 322)
23. ______________ are persistent thoughts that an individual may recognize as irrational but still cannot stop thinking.	obsessions (p. 322)
24. A __________ is an __________ that an individual feels he must carry out even though he regards it as a waste of time or ________________.	compulsion; act; foolish (p. 322)
25. Many neurotic compulsions are directly tied to feelings of ____________ or ____________.	guilt; fear; (p. 322)
26. All compulsions are ________ neurotic. For example, Benjamin Franklin was said to have worked sixteen to ________ hours per day.	not; eighteen (p. 322)
27. ____________________ is marked by symptoms of ____________________ in the absence of actual ________________ disturbance.	hysterical neurosis; physical disability; organic (p. 323)
28. Anxiety resulting from a ____________ situation and "converted" into ______________ symptoms is referred to as __________________ reaction.	stressful; physical; conversion (p. 323)
29. Freud attributed hysterical symptoms to the ________ of ____________ and mis directed ______________ energy.	expression; repressed; sexual (p. 323)
30. Freud treated hysteria with __________________.	hypnosis (p. 324)

31. ______________ is a ____________ common hysterical reaction than other types.	dissociative reaction; less (p. 324)
32. Total or ______________ inability to remember past personal experiences is known as ____________.	partial; amnesia (p. 324)
33. Amnesia can either be either organic or ____________ (functional). In the previous case the amnesia would not be considered ______________.	psychological; neurotic (p. 324)
34. *Three Faces of Eve* was a book and a movie that portrays an example of ______________.	multiple personality (p. 325)
35. ______________, or sleepwalking, occurs mostly among ______________.	somnambulism; children (p. 325)
36. ______________, which are caused by emotional factors, are characterized by actual ______________ damage or ______________.	psychosomatic disorders; physiological; change (p. 327)
37. __________ as many women as men get __________.	one fourth; ulcers (p. 328)
38. ____________ and ____________ are prime factors in causing ______________.	tension; worry; ulcers (p. 328)
39. Most headaches are a result of ______________.	nervous tension (p. 328)
40. ______________ are accompanied by a dilation of ______________ arteries.	migraine headaches; cranial (p. 328)
41. Migraine headaches are usually traced to an unhappy situation with one's ____________ or ____________ or some other equally demanding situation.	job; marriage (p. 328)
42. ______ times more women than men have ________ headaches.	two; migraine (p. 328)
43. When no ____________ cause of ____________ high blood pressure can be found, the disorder is referred to as ______________.	physical; chronic; essential hypertension (p. 328)

44. ______________ is assumed to be the ________ result of ______________.

essential hypertension; direct; stress (p. 329)

45. ______________ is considered the ____________ serious of all behavior disorders.

psychosis; most (p. 330)

46. For the ______________, reality and his __________ world are ____________________.

psychotic; dream; indistinguishable (p. 330)

47. A ____________ is a false belief that a person maintains even when presented with ______________ or ______________ to the contrary.

delusion; logic, evidence (p. 331)

48. ________________ refer to sounds and voices which a person perceives that do not exist.

hallucinations (p. 331)

49. The ______________ behavior is characterized by gross ________________ disturbances, including delusions and ____________________.

schizophrenic's; thought; hallucinations (p. 331)

50. For the most part the four types of schizophrenia ________________ exist in pure form.

do not (p. 332)

51. ____________ schizophrenia has its onset usually during or shortly after ____________________.

simple; puberty (p. 332)

52. The ____________ schizophrenic is characterized by ____________ swings in ____________, ranging from extreme ______________ to wild ______________.

catatonic; wide; mood; withdrawal; excitement (p. 332)

53. One of the most common forms of schizophrenia is ____________________.

paranoid schizophrenia (p. 334)

54. A paranoid schizophrenic may exhibit delusions of ______________ or ____________.

persecution; grandeur (p. 334)

55. ____________ is marked by less obvious ____________ disorganization.

paranoia; personality (p. 335)

56. The ________ functions almost normally unless having a ________ episode.	paranoia; delusional (p. 335)
57. The development of paranoia usually involves a long history of ________, ________, and ________.	aloofness; suspicion; stubbornness (p. 336)
58. A third major psychosis which is best characterized as an ________ of mood — either elation or deep depression is ________.	exaggeration; affective psychosis (p. 337)
59. A person who experiences the mood of a ________ psychotic has a ________ sense of ________ ________ similar to a person who has been on ________.	manic; tremendous; well-being; "speed" (p. 337)
60. A ________ psychosis is much more ________ than manic ________.	depressive; common; psychosis (p. 337)
61. The main difference between neurotic ________ and psychotic depression is that ________ depression is accompanied by ________, ________, and ________.	depression; psychotic; guilt; sin; disease (p. 337)
62. The onset of ________ depression is usually ________ and cannot be traced to any specific event while ________ depression comes on ________ as the result of some specific event.	psychotic; gradual; neurotic; suddenly (p. 338)
63. ________ psychosis is quite ________ in northern ________ but ________ in the United States.	manic-depression; common; Europe; rare (p. 338)
64. Most attempted ________ are done by people who are seriously ________.	suicides; depressed (p. 338)

65. Almost ________ as many ____________ attempt ____________, but ________ times more men than women ______________.	twice; women; suicide; three; succeed (p. 339)
66. Clinicians feel that the best ______________ of a depressed person's potential ________ is when that person tells someone he is going to ______ it.	indicator; suicide; try (p. 340)
67. An anti social ______________________ to learn from his ____________________.	personality; fails; mistakes (p. 341)
68. Among the most abused of the addictive substances are ______________ and ______________.	alcohol; heroin (p. 341)
69. ____________ is the most serious ____________ health problem in the United States.	alcoholism; mental (p. 341)
70. The long term efforts of alcoholism include ________ ________, ______________________, ____________ ____________, ______________________, and high ____________ rates.	absenteeism; poor job performance; unhappy marriages; broken homes; accident (p. 342)
71. The ______________ has a behavioral cycle similar to that of an ____________. He eats to __________ tension.	"foodaholic"; alcoholic; reduce (p. 343)
72. ___________ addiction is one of the leading causes of crimes such as __________ and ______________.	heroin; theft; prostitution (p. 344)
73. ____________, ____________ ("reds"), ____________ ("yellow jackets") are barbiturates which pose a danger to health today.	phenobarbital; seconal; nembutal (p. 344)
74. ______________ and ______________ are two of the common amphetamides on the market today.	benzedrine; dexedrine (p. 345)
75. Psychological treatment of homosexuals who are motivated to become __________________ has been effective in only ____________ of the cases reported.	heterosexual; one-fourth (p. 349)

76. Down's ______ is a result of a ______ disorder in which there are ______ rather than the usual ______ chromosomes.	syndrome; genetic forty-seven; forty-six (p. 349)
77. The ______ is characterized by ______, ______, ______ and ______ mental and physical underdevelopment.	cretin; apathy; thickening of the skin; defective speech; general (p. 349)
78. The causes of microcephaly are ______	unknown (p. 350)

KEYS TO SELF MASTERY

ABNORMAL BEHAVIOR

1. coping
2. Thomas Szasz
3. maladaptive behavior
4. psychopathology
5. deviant behavior
6. emotional disturbance
7. mental illness

ATTITUDES TOWARD ABNORMAL BEHAVIOR

EXPLANATIONS OF ABNORMAL BEHAVIOR

1. psychodynamic model
2. biomedical model
3. general paresis
4. Wassermann
5. XYY
6. social learning model
7. existential model

NEUROSIS

1. anxiety
2. phobias
3. obsessive - compulsive
4. obsessions
5. hysterical neurosis
6. conversion reaction
7. dissociative reaction
8. amnesia

9. fugue state
10. multiple personality
11. somnambulism
12. depressive neurosis

PSYCHOSOMATIC DISORDERS

1. psychosomatic
2. ulcers
3. migraine headaches
4. hypertension

PSYCHOSIS

1. delusions
2. hallucinations
3. functional psychoses
4. organic psychoses

SCHIZOPHRENIA

1. simple schizophrenia
2. catatonic schizophrenia
4. paranoid schizophrenia
5. delusion of grandeur

PARANOIA

AFFECTIVE PSYCHOSIS

1. manic psychosis
2. depressive psychosis
3. manic - depressive psychosis
4. involutional psychosis

PERSONALITY DISORDERS

1. antisocial personality
2. addictions
3. psychological dependence
4. physiological dependence
5. alcoholism
7. delirium tremens
8. "foodaholic"
9. methadone
10. barbiturates
11. amphetamides
12. sexual deviations

13. impotence
14. frigidity
15. masochism
16. exhibitionism
17. fetishism
18. pedophilia
19. voyeurism
20. incest
21. sadism
22. prostitution
23. transvestism
24. transsexualism
25. homosexuality

MENTAL RETARDATION

1. primary mental retardation
2. Down's syndrome (mongolism)
3. cretinism
4. microcephaly
5. phenyketonuria (PKU)

SELF QUIZ

1. Psychopathological behavior: — a

   a. refers to a tremendous range of behaviors
   b. is best described in terms of subjective discomfort
   c. includes all behaviors that deviate from the norm
   d. is usually adaptive behavior

2. Psychological problems can be caused by: — d

   a. brain damage
   b. chemical or hormonal imbalances
   c. genetic defects
   d. all of the above

3. Hormone imbalances are the main cause of: — d

   a. homosexuality
   b. impotence
   c. frigidity
   d. none of the above

4. The conversion of a psychological problem into an organic symptom is a characteristic of: — c

   a. organic psychosis
   b. anxiety reaction
   c. hysteria
   d. introversion

5. An obsessive condition involves: — c

   a. delusions
   b. hallucinations
   c. recurrence of unwanted ideas
   d. conversion reactions

6. The most common form of neurosis is: — d

   a. hysteria
   b. obsessive - compulsive
   c. phobia
   d. anxiety reaction

7. The largest and most meaningless diagnostic category is: — b

   a. organic psychosis
   b. schizophrenia
   c. affective psychosis
   d. neurosis

8. Which of the following is *not* a condition classed as a social disorder? — c

   a. sociopath
   b. psychopath
   c. schizophrenia
   d. perversion

9. Sexual offenders who inflict physical harm to people tend to be: — d

   a. psychotic
   b. under - sexed
   c. narrow-minded
   d. all of the above

10. The earliest explanations of mental illness saw people as: — d

    a. evil
    b. ruined by childhood experiences
    c. genetically defective
    d. possessed by devils

11. Which of the following is *not* a major criteria for defining mental illness? — d

    a. statistical deviation
    b. personal maladjustment
    c. cultural deviation
    d. criminal behavior

12. "Mental illness" is: — d

    a. clearly differentiated from mental health
    b. seldom curable
    c. due to heredity alone
    d. more common than most people realize

13. There is presently a movement away from the classification of deviates because: — d

    a. labeling gives the false impression of certainty
    b. labeling is too rigid to reflect the great variation of human reactions
    c. labeling is too time consuming
    d. a and b

14. Which of the following is *not* true about psychosis? — c

    a. It is usually more severe than neurosis
    b. It usually develops suddenly
    c. Psychotics can still distinguish fact from fantasy
    d. Psychotics generally do not display the anxiety so characteristic of neurotics

15. Sensory impressions of external objects in the absence of any appropriate stimulus are called: — b

    a. catatonic episodes
    b. hallucinations
    c. delusions
    d. illusions

16. Amnesia is a form of the rare reactions — d
    a. conversion
    b. hypochondriac
    c. phobic
    d. dissociative

17. Multiple personality refers to the extremely rare cases of dissociative reactions in which a person: — b
    a. has broken his personality down into multiple components
    b. has two or more complete but alternating personalities
    c. has amnesia and flees to another city to live as an entirely different person
    d. developed a "glove" anesthesia

18. Depressive neurosis is attributed to: — d
    a. an anger turned inward
    b. an ideal self that seems impossibly distant
    c. a lack of positive reinforcement in the person's life
    d. all of the above depending on whether the theory is Freudian, Rogerian, or Behavioristic respectively

19. A TV singing commercial that persists in running through one's head is a mild: — d
    a. fantasy
    b. conversion reaction
    c. compulsion
    d. obsession

20. A sociopath is: — b
    a. a moral imbecile
    b. an antisocial individual above average in intelligence and in the manipulation of others
    c. a person's particular way of obtaining social prestige
    d. usually very repentent for his misdeeds and has the lowest record for repeating

21. Contrary to popular belief: a

    a. alcohol is a depressant
    b. sexual desire is increased at all levels of alcoholic intoxication
    c. alcoholics have learned their maladaptive method in order to cope with their unusual stresses
    d. all of the above

22. Alcoholics: b

    a. experience no withdrawal symptoms when they are deprived of alcohol
    b. tend to be immature, impulsive individuals with low self-esteem and display an inability to tolerate failure
    c. are effectively being treated with the traditional psychotherapeutic techniques
    d. are perhaps treated least successfully by alcoholics anonymous

23. The *main* problem in the treatment of drug addicts, alcoholics, or sociopaths is that: a

    a. most like their life style, i.e., they don't want help
    b. they are almost impossible to locate
    c. there are few of these people who can afford the price of modern therapists
    d. there are too many of them coming in for help in the already understaffed medical and psychiatric facilities

24. The causes of homosexuality: b

    a. are now known to be certain heredity and psychological factors
    b. probably include lack of opportunity, seduction, and fear of the opposite sex
    c. are relatively simple and easy to remedy
    d. none of the above

25. The sexual deviation in which interest is focused on something inanimate is: b

    a. bestiality
    b. fetishism
    c. masochism
    d. pedophilia

26. Suicide: — d

    a. is most prevalent at the lowest levels of depression
    b. rates are highest during periods of dreary weather
    c. is much more prevalent among women than men
    d. all of the above

27. A person whose behavior is characterized by loss of contact with reality, hallucinations, and delusions is probably: — c

    a. neurotic
    b. a sexual deviate
    c. psychotic
    d. incurable

28. Schizophrenia is manifested in part by: — c

    a. increased awareness of reality
    b. disturbed thought processes but normal emotional reactions
    c. withdrawal from interpersonal relationships
    d. personalization

29. All of the following are : alcohol, barbiturates, bromides. — c

    a. antipsychotics
    b. amphetamides
    c. sedatives
    d. tranquilizers

30. Catatonic schizophrenia: — d

    a. may be a reactive process type
    b. is characterized by prolonged periods of motionlessness
    c. may involve periodic rages
    d. all of the above

APPROACHES TO PSYCHOTHERAPY

In our complex and highly organized modern world, open displays of rage, anger, and hostility are increasingly tabooed; they are considered irrational. Driven underground (repressed), man's inevitable feelings of aggression seek less direct forms of expression: they are turned against the self, producing angry depression; they are expressed interpersonally in backbiting, viciousness, and cruel hostility. Equally important our repressed aggression is projected onto others. No matter how we deny or repress the hostility that is in us, it is impossible to go through a day without being blocked, rejected, criticized, or ignored. To continue to repress the hostility produces increasing anxiety. Many new interventions or psychotherapies such as encounter groups, TM, biofeedback, and human potential seminars have evolved to help man cope or "pull himself back together again."

OBJECTIVES FOR STUDY

OBJECTIVE A. Be able to define:

1. psychotherapy ______________________ p. 357

____

____

2. psychoanalysis ______________________ p. 362

____

____

3. transference ______ p. 362

4. anorexia nervosa ______ p. 366

5. hyperventilate ______ p. 368

6. crossed transaction ______ p. 374

7. *parent* ______ p. 374

8. *adult* ______ p. 374

9. *child* ______ p. 374

10. crossed transaction ______ p. 374

11. a "game" ______________________ p. 375

12. involuntary commitment ______________________ p. 377

13. voluntary commitment ______________________ p. 377

14. hypnosis ______________________ p. 379

15. hyperkinetic ______________________ p. 382

OBJECTIVE B. Be able to identify:

1. Arthur Janov ______________________ p. 359

2. free association ______________________ p. 362

3. wish fulfillment ______________________ p. 363

4. Karl Rogers ______ p. 363

5. self theory ______ p. 364

6. symptom substitution ______ p. 367

7. desensitization therapy ______ p. 368

8. aversion therapy ______ p. 369

9. A. A. Lazarus ______ p. 369

10. observation therapy ______ p. 370

11. group therapy ______ p. 371

12. family therapy ______ p. 372

13. interpersonal model of man ______ p. 373

14. interpersonal therapy ______ p. 374

15. TA ______ p. 374

16. Eric Berne (1961) ______ p. 374

17. *Games People Play* ______ p. 374

18. ego states (Berne) ______ p. 374

19. human potential movement ______ p. 376

20. halfway house ______ p. 377

21. family care units ______ p. 377

22. sedatives ______ p. 378

23. tranquilizers ______ p. 378

24. antidepressants ______ p. 378

25. antipsychotics ______ p. 378

26. electro shock therapy ______ p. 379

27. marathon hypnotherapy ______ p. 380

28. EMG ______ p. 380

29. biofeedback ______ p. 380

30. *frontalis* muscle ______ p. 380

31. EEG ______ p. 380

32. alpha waves ______ p. 382

33. theta waves ______ p. 382

34. genetic counseling ______ p. 383

35. Perry London ______ p. 384

36. age of repression ______________________ p. 384

37. age of anxiety ______________________ p. 384

38. age of ennui ______________________ p. 384

39. TM ______________________ p. 387

OBJECTIVE C. Be able to discuss the different means of referrals to psychotherapy p. 357-358

OBJECTIVE D. Be able to name and give the educational requirements for mental health personnel. p. 360; 361

1. ______________________

2. ______________________________

____

____

3. ______________________________

____

____

4. ______________________________

____

____

5. ______________________________

____

____

6. ______________________________

____

____

7.

a. ______________________________

b. ______________________________

c. ______________________________

d. ______________________________

e. ______________________________

f. ______________________________

OBJECTIVE E. Be able to compare and contrast psychoanalysis and client-centered therapy. p. 362-365

OBJECTIVE F. Be able to compare and contrast psychoanalysis and behavior therapy p. 362-363; 365-371

OBJECTIVE G. Be able to relate the theory relative to desensitization therapy and give an example. p. 368

OBJECTIVE H. Be able to compare and contrast group therapy and family therapy

p. 371-373

OBJECTIVE I. Be able to list and give an example of behavior which corresponds to the three ego states of Berne

p. 374

1.

2.

3.

OBJECTIVE J. Be able to identify and discuss four adjuncts to psychotherapy

p. 376-383

1. ______________________________

2. ______________________________

3. ______________________________

4. ______________________________

OBJECTIVE K. Be able to state and recognize criteria for hospitalization.

p. 376-377

OBJECTIVE L. Be able to list four drug categories used as an adjunct to psychotherapy. Give the names of specific drugs in each category and tell the effect.

p. 378

1.

2.

3.

4. ______________________________

____

____

____

____

OBJECTIVE M. Be able to give the historical perspective of psychotherapy according to Perry London. p. 384-385

1. ______________________________

____

____

____

2. ______________________________

____

____

____

3. ______________________________

____

____

____

OBJECTIVE N. Be able to recall relevant material relative to "Keys To Self Mastery."

PROGRAMMED REVIEW

1. ________________ is a general term referring to the use of psychological knowledge and ________________ in the treatment of behavior disorders.	psychotherapy; techniques (p. 357)
2. Therapists today generally use a combination of ________________ better known as an eclectic approach.	techniques (p. 359)

3. Freud theorized that personality disorders arise in part because we________ unacceptable and ________ thoughts and ________.	repress; painful; impulses (p. 362)
4. The analyst's task is to help the patient achieve ________ into the ________ conflicts that are causing his ________ problems and to help him experience the ________ associated with the ________ event.	insight; unconscious; behavior; emotion; original (p. 362)
5. The chief tool of psychoanalysis is called ________ ________.	free association (p. 362)
6. The purpose of psychoanalysis is to ________ the patient's ________ so that he can cope with his unconscious ________ and thus control his his ________.	strengthen; ego; impulses; anxiety (p. 362)
7. The patient's tendency to respond to the ________ as he did to his parents and others close to him in ________.	analyst; childhood (p. 362)
8. Freud felt that ________ express ________ fulfillment, things we wish would happen.	dreams; wish (p. 363)
9. Psychoanalysis may require as many as ________ years, with ________ to ________ sessions per weeks.	seven; four; five (p. 363)
10. ________ believes that man has an ________ drive to seek ________.	Rogers; inherent; self-actualization (p. 363)
11. The goal of the Rogerian therapist is to set up a ________ environment by displaying ________ and ________.	non-threatening; warmth; acceptance (p. 364)

12. According to Rogers, it is important for the individual to have ______ into his present situation and to be able to ______ the way he feels "right now."	insight; express (p. 364)
13. The Rogerian therapist never ______ or suggests a ______ to a problem, instead he leave the solution up to the ______ and ______ whatever solution the individual reaches.	advises; solution; client; accepts (p. 364)
14. Achieving ______ into one's ______ and behavior tendencies is ______ always sufficient to ______ one's behavior.	insight; problems; not; change (p. 365)
15. Behavior therapists seek behavior ______, not ______ for their clients.	change; insight
16. Behaviorists reject the term ______ and maintain that behavior problems are the result of ______ and can therefore be extinguished.	personality disorders; learning (p. 365)
17. Studies have revealed that ______ usually does not occur when behavior therapy is used.	symptom substitution (p. 367)
18. A technique that uses the concepts of ______ conditioning in reducing ______ and ______ is called ______.	classical; fears; phobias; desensitization (p. 368)
19. Behavior therapists view the homosexual behavior as a ______ of the ______ sex.	phobic avoidance; opposite (p. 369)
20. When ______ conditioning procedures are used to modify ______ behavior, it is called ______ therapy.	avoidance; unwanted; aversion (p. 369)
21. ______ therapy usually involves from ______ to ______ people, including the therapist.	Group; three; twenty (p. 371)

22. Learning about each ________ in ________ therapy is often the first step toward improving family ________.	other; family; communication (p. 373)
23. The ________, ________, and ________ are the three ego states according to ________.	parent; adult; child; Berne (p. 374)
24. The ________ movement emphasizes increasing ________, enriching our lives, and freeing us from social ________ in hopes of fostering more intimate and fulfilling ________.	human potential; self-awareness; emotional; facades; personal relationships (p. 376)
25. ________ is a legal procedure for getting a person sent to a mental hospital ________ his permission.	involuntary commitment; without (p. 377)
26. The emphasis behind ________ commitment is on ________ patients to recover.	voluntary; *expecting* (p. 377)
27. It is relatively easy for a person to become ________ on ________ and ________.	dependent; sedatives; tranquilizers (p. 378)
28. ________ generally are not as effective as the tranquilizers and have little ________ on the less severe forms of depression such as ________ depression.	anti depressants; effect; neurotic (p. 378)
29. In ________ the patient feels no pain and wakes up after a few minutes quite ________.	EST; relaxed (p. 379)
30. ________ is an extremely important variable in any treatment procedure.	relaxation (p. 380)
31. The ________ is a very important indicator of the amount of ________ an individual is experiencing from moment to moment.	frontalis muscle; relaxation (p. 380)

32. Many unpleasant physical symptoms such as________ ______________, _________________, and__________ __________________can be successfully treated by learning to relax through_____________________.	tension headaches; insomnia; essential hypertension; biofeedback (p. 381)
33. Two of the most widely used preventive techniques are____________________________ and_______________.	crisis intervention; education (p. 383)
34. The three distinct historical periods, according to Perry London, are the_________________________, the _______________, and the present__________________.	age of repression; age of anxiety; age of ennuic (p. 384)
35. Psychologists are helping in this age of boredom through intervention with__________________________ such as_________________________, and______________ __________________.	new techniques, encounter groups; relaxation therapies (p. 387)

KEYS TO SELF MASTERY

PSYCHOTHERAPY

1. psychoanalysts
2. psychiatrists
3. clinical psychologists
4. counselors
5. psychiatric social workers
6. psychiatric nurses
7. nonprofessionals

PSYCHOANALYSIS

1. free association
2. transference
3. wish fulfillment
4. dreams
5. slips of the tongue

CLIENT-CENTERED THERAPY

SELF THEORY

BEHAVIOR THERAPY

1. anorexia nervosa
2. modification
3. desensitization therapy
4. aversion therapy
5. hyperventilate
6. A. A. Lazarus
7. observation therapy

GROUP THERAPY

FAMILY THERAPY

INTERPERSONAL THERAPY: TRANSACTIONAL ANALYSIS

1. interpersonal therapy
2. TA
3. *parent*
4. *adult*
5. *child*
6. crossed transaction
7. a "game"
8. human potential movement

ADJUNCTS TO PSYCHOTHERAPY

1. hospitalization
2. involuntary commitment
3. voluntary commitment
4. halfway house
5. family care units
6. drugs
7. sedatives
8. tranquilizers
9. anti depressants
10. antipsychotics
11. electroshock therapy
12. hypnosis
13. biofeedback techniques
14. *frontalis muscle*
15. EMG
16. EEG
17. alpha waves
18. theta waves
19. hyperkinetic

PREVENTION OF ABNORMAL BEHAVIOR

1. crisis intervention
2. education
3. genetic counseling

PSYCHOTHERAPY IN HISTORICAL PERSPECTIVE

1. Perry London
2. age of repression
3. age of anxiety
4. age of ennui
5. zen
6. encounter groups
7. massage and breathing therapies
8. TM

SELF QUIZ

1. The psychologist who solicits clients, advertises services, and promises results: b

   a. will do a poor business, since most people do not trust that kind of an approach
   b. is probably a "quack" and in violation of the ethical standards of psychologists
   c. must be registered with the American Psychological Association
   d. all of the above

2. Primary treatment of the mental health problem focuses on the ____, while secondary treatment consists of some form of ____ on existing psychopathological problems. b

   a. symptoms; depth therapy
   b. elimination of basic causes; crisis therapy
   c. after effects of emotional problems; rehabilitation
   d. individual; group marathon

3. The technique of free association: b
   a. involves clients saying the first thing that comes to mind when the therapist reads a list of words, one at a time
   b. is designed to uncover areas of unconscious resistence or blocking
   c. is used to help the patient understand the contents of his conscious mind
   d. is relatively easy for a client to learn

4. Dream analysis is a part of: c
   a. nondirective therapy
   b. directive therapy
   c. psychoanalytic therapy
   d. action therapy

5. Rogerian therapy is characterized, at least in part by: a
   a. the emphasis on the self-concept
   b. its highly intellectual rather than affective (emotional) approach
   c. the therapist's assumption of a role as interpreter, teacher, and guide
   d. conditional, positive regard

6. Two important aspects of psychoanalysis are the therapist's ______ of ______, and the ______ of the conflict. c
   a. impressions; the patient; free association
   b. resolutions; dependence; effective repression
   c. interpretations; dreams; working through
   d. slips; the tongue; transference

7. To say the Rogerian therapist is *congruent* means to say that he is b
   a. friendly
   b. genuine
   c. empathetic
   d. accredited

8. Behavior therapy: a
   - a. deals directly with the disturbed behavior
   - b. tends to go on for years
   - c. has drastically declined in popularity
   - d. all of the above

9. In implosive therapy: b
   - a. the client is allowed to escape from the situation as soon as he feels he can no longer stand the anxiety.
   - b. only the most anxiety-producing scenes are described and imagined
   - c. anxiety increases gradually with each repetition of the frightening story until it reaches a climax and suddenly disappears.
   - d. the person learns to change his behavior through posthypnotic suggestion

10. The process wherein the behavior therapist pairs an incompatible response, such as relaxation, with an anxiety-provoking stimulus is called: b
    - a. classified conditioning
    - b. reciprocal inhibition
    - c. empathy
    - d. experimental neurosis

11. Enuresis: d
    - a. refers to night bedwetting
    - b. is fairly common in children
    - c. can be effectively treated in 70-90 percent of the cases using classical conditioning principles.
    - d. all of the above

12. The major advantage of tranquilizers over sedatives is the fact that tranquilizers: d
    - a. are much less expensive
    - b. affect behavior much more quickly
    - c. reduce anxiety and tension
    - d. do not induce drowsiness or sleep

13. The major unfortunate shortcoming of drug therapy or shock therapy is that: c

    a. it is expensive
    b. is very time consuming
    c. the improvements are only temporary
    d. they require a large staff of medically trained personnel

14. A fundamental aspect of all sensitivity and encounter groups is: a

    a. genuine open interaction and self-disclosure
    b. nudity
    c. to break down defenses and roles with fatigue
    d. for each member of the group to try to shock the other members by telling them his innermost secrets and desires.

15. Which of the following is **not** among current trends in mental health: a

    a. building more and larger state mental hospitals
    b. giving patients more freedom to govern themselves
    c. voluntary commitment
    d. providing a wider variety of services to patients

16. Which of the following is *least* important as a contributing factor in a therapist's success rate: a

    a. the school of therapy
    b. the amount experience the therapist has
    c. accurate empathy
    d. nonpossessive warmth and genuineness

17. Clinical and counseling psychologists are more qualified than psychiatrists to administer psychological tests and conduct psychological research. On the other hand they are not trained as physicians and they are not qualified to d

    a. engage in psychotherapy
    b. treat functional psychoses
    c. interpret the findings of psychological tests and diagnose mental patients
    d. prescribe drugs

18. Transference occurs when the patient — d
    a. becomes aware of his unconscious motives and wishes
    b. is able to adjust to the stresses of daily life
    c. experiences emotional upheavals during psychoanalytic sessions
    d. reacts to the therapist as if he were some other important person in his life.

19. Which of the following is *not* an important element of the traditional psychoanalytic method? — b
    a. free association
    b. reinforcement
    c. transference
    d. dream analysis

20. A patient is lying on a couch with his eyes closed. The therapist asks him to imagine himself standing in a room full of people; then he pauses five seconds and asks the patient to raise his finger if he felt any disturbance while imagining this scene. This example illustrates — d
    a. free association
    b. client-centered counseling
    c. rational-emotive therapy
    d. systematic desensitization

21. At three years of age a child developed a habit of throwing food during his meals. In an effort to eliminate this behavior, his mother would remove all of the remaining food whenever this behavior occurred. After a few abbreviated meals, the child's behavior improved markedly. This example illustrates the use of — a
    a. aversive technique
    b. desensitization
    c. somatotherapy
    d. eclectic therapy

22. One of the major values of chemotherapy is that it — c

a. can completely cure many psychological disorders
b. need not be administered by a professional and is available to everyone
c. has reduced much of the need for restraint and isolation in mental hospitals
d. enables the therapist to predict the results of his treatment accurately.

23. The major tranquilizing drugs which reduce hallucination, delusions, and aggressive behavior are known as ___ drugs. — a

a. antipsychotic
b. antianxiety
c. anti depressant
d. mood-elevating

24. The EEG and EMG are important concepts in — b

a. encounter groups
b. biofeedback therapy
c. unconscious motivation therapy
d. psychoanalysis

25. The most effective therapeutic technique is — b

a. behavior therapy
b. one which has been selected in accordance with important patient and therapist variables
c. psychoanalysis
d. chemotherapy